COLLEGE OUTLINE SERIES

GENERAL
BOTANY

HARRY J. FULLER

Fourth Edition

BARNES & NOBLE, Inc., **New York**

Booksellers • **Publishers** • **Since 1873**

The Author

Harry J. Fuller received the M.S. and Ph.D. degrees from Washington University and the Missouri Botanical Garden, and did graduate work at the University of Wisconsin. He has taught botany at the University of Illinois since 1932, except for the period 1942-1945, when he served the U.S. government as a rubber specialist in South America. Professor Fuller has made research contributions to the study of effects of radiations on plants, plant ecology of South America, photoperiodism, and natural rubber production. His published books include *The Plant World,* a text for one-semester botany courses, and *College Botany* (with a co-author) for one-year courses in botany.

Printed in the United States of America

Preface

This book, like others in the College Outline Series, is a condensed study-guide, intended for use with standard textbooks in the field. The "Quick Reference Table" gives page references in several textbooks of botany to the subjects treated in this outline. The sequence of topics is that usually followed in college courses of elementary botany. Such arrangement facilitates the use of this outline as a supplement to any course regardless of the particular text being used.

This Outline is in no sense a textbook in itself. In an introduction to another book in this same Series, Professor C. C. Crawford of the University of Southern California described the proper use of Outlines as follows: "As a type of educational literature, the syllabus, or outline, has a distinct service and value, if properly used. It gives order, organization, and perspective to a field of study. It gives definiteness, objectivity, and tangible qualities to the subject or course. It provides the student with something to which he can cling. It enables the teacher and the student to define the limits of the course. The teacher can know when the material has been covered completely; the student has a checking guide by which to judge the adequacy of his study and preparation."

The author wishes to thank Mary L. Fuller and Wilson N. Stewart, who prepared most of the diagrams and drawings. Thanks are due Dr. Gordon Alexander for permission to use some of the illustrations in his *General Biology*, published by Barnes and Noble, Inc. The author acknowledges with thanks the criticisms by Dr. Oswald Tippo of certain chapters in the book.

—H. J. F.

Urbana, Illinois

TABULATED BIBLIOGRAPHY OF STANDARD TEXTBOOKS

This Outline is keyed to standard textbooks in two ways.

1. If you are studying one of the following textbooks, consult the cross references here listed to find which pages of the Outline summarize the appropriate chapter of your text. (Roman numerals refer to the textbook chapters, Arabic figures to the corresponding Outline pages.)

2. If you are using the Outline as your basis for study and need a fuller treatment of a topic, consult the pages of any of the standard textbooks as indicated in the Quick Reference Table on pp. viii-ix.

Coulter and Dittmer, *The Story of the Plant Kingdom,* 1959, Univ. of Chicago.
I (1–6); II (7–10); III (10, 40–41, 61–70); IV (9–10, 38–60); V (9, 31–37); VI (11, 17–19, 67–68, 78–83, 170–171); VII (107–114); VIII (109–111, 115–123); IX (110, 117, 120–123); X (7–8, 109–111, 127–129); XI (8, 77, 109–111, 124–136, 166, 172); XII (163–169); XIII (9, 109–110, 137–143); XIV (138–139, 144–162); XV (7–8, 146–151); XVI (109–110, 152–156, 166–168); XVII (156–162); XVIII (9–10, 84–91, 159–162); XIX (92–98, 158–162); XX (170–176); XXI (163–169).

Emerson, F. W., *Basic Botany,* 1954, McGraw-Hill.
I (1–3); II (4–27); III (61–71); IV (72–77); V (72–76); VI (23, 68–69); VII (28–37); VIII (38–60); IX (78–83); X (99–106); XI (163–169); XII (107–114); XIII (115–116, 124–126); XIV (120–123); XV (116–120); XVI (127–136); XVII (137–143); XVIII (144–151); XIX (152–156); XX (156–159); XXI (84–98, 159–162); XXII and XXIII (170–176).

Fuller, H. J., *The Plant World,* 3rd ed., 1955, Holt.
I (1–6); II (94–98); III (7–10); IV (11–19); V (20–27); VI (28–37); VII (38–43); VIII (44–54); IX (50–52); X (55–60); XI (61–67); XII (67–71); XIII (72–77); XIV (78–83); XV (84–91); XVI (92–94); XVII (99–106); XVIII (107–114); XIX (115–123); XX (124–126); XXI (127–136); XXII (137–143); XXIII (144–145); XXIV (146–149); XXV (150–151); XXVI (152–156); XXVII (156–159); XXVIII (159–162); XXIX (163–169); XXX (170–176); XXXI (177–183).

Fuller and Tippo, *College Botany,* rev. ed., 1954, Holt.
I (1–3); II (4–6); III (7–9); IV (94–98); V (9–10); VI (11–19); VII (20–27); VIII (28–31); IX (31–37); X (38–43); XI (44–54); XII (49–52); XIII (55–60); XIV (61–67); XV (67–71); XVI (72–77); XVII (78–83); XVIII (84–91); XIX (92–94); XX (99–106); XXI (107–114); XXII (115–123); XXIII (124–126); XXIV (127–136); XXV (133–182); XXVI (137–143); XXVII (144–145); XXVIII (146–149); XXIX (150–151); XXX (152–156); XXXI (156–159); XXXII (159–162); XXXIII (163–169); XXXIV (170–176); XXXV (177–183).

Haupt, *An Introduction to Botany,* 3rd ed., 1956, McGraw-Hill.
I (1–10, 107–114); II (11–19); III (20–27); IV (28–37); V (38–43); VI (44–60); VII (61–71); VIII (72–77); IX (77–83); X (170–176); XI (84–98); XII (86–88); XIII (94–98); XIV (99–106); XV (163–169); XVI (115–123); XVII (124–136); XVIII (137–143); XIX (146–156); XX (156–162); XXI (168–169).

Hill, et al., *Botany: A Textbook for Colleges,* 2nd ed., 1950, McGraw-Hill.
I (1–3, 7–10); II (11–15); III (11–19); IV (61–71); V (72–77); VI (28–37); VII (20–27); VIII (38–60); IX (20–27, 78–83); X (84–91); XI (92–98); XII (72–77); XIII (107–114); XIV (115–123); XV (124–136); XVI (137–143); XVII (144–156); XVIII (152–162); XIX (159–161); XX (99–106).

Northen, *Introductory Plant Science,* 1958, Ronald Press.
I (177–183); II (7–10); III (94–98); IV (11–19); V (20–27); VI (67–69); VII (72–77); VIII (61–67); IX (20–24, 68–70, 171); X (31–37); XI (28–31); XII (38–49, 52–54); XIII (49–52); XIV (55–60); XV (72–77); XVI (25–27, 78–83); XVII (79); XVIII (59–60, 112); XIX (84–88); XX (88–91); XXI (92–98); XXII (84); XXIII, XXIV, and XXV (99–106); XXVI and XXVII (170–176); XXIX (163–169); XXX (107–114); XXXI (115–123); XXXII (124–126); XXXV (127–136); XXXVI (137–143); XXXVII (144–151); XXXVIII (152–156); XXXIX (156–159); XL (159–162).

Robbins, Weier, and Stocking, *Botany,* 2nd ed., 1957, Wiley.
I (1–3); II (7–18, 170–183); III (107–114); IV (9–10); V (11–27); VI (38–54); VII (31–37); VIII (61–67); IX (28–30, 72); X (55–60); XI (67–77); XII (84–91); XIII (92–98); XIV (99–106); XV (78–83); XVI (107–114); XVII (115–116, 124–126); XVIII (116–123); XIX (127–129); XX (129–136); XXII (137–143); XXIII (144–151); XXIV (152–159); XXV (159–162); XXVI (163–169).

Sinnott and Wilson, *Botany: Principles and Problems,* 1955, McGraw-Hill.
I (3–6); II (1–5); III (7–10); IV (11–19); V (20–37); VI (61–71); VII (38–60); VIII (72–77); IX (25–27, 78–83); XI (81–83, 170–172); XII (170–176); XIII (84–98); XIV (99–106); XV (163–169); XVI (107–114); XVII (115–123); XVIII (124–136); XIX (137–143); XX (144–145); XXI (146–149); XXII (150–151); XXIII (152–156); XXIV (156–159); XXV (159–162).

Smith et al., *A Textbook of General Botany,* 1953, Macmillan.
I (1–6); II (9–10); III (11–25); IV (25–27); V (28–37); VI and VII (38–53); VIII (61–67); IX (67–77); X (55–58, 68–69); XI (78–83); XII (107–111, 163–169); XIII (112–114); XIV through XVII (115–123); XVIII through XXIII (124–136); XXIV & XXV (137–143); XXVI (144–151); XXVII (152–156); XXVIII (156–159); XXIX (84–91, 159–162); XXX (92–98); XXXI (164, 168–169); XXXIII (170–176).

Taylor and Weber, *General Botany,* 1956, Van Nostrand.
I (1–5); II (20–21); III (11–27); IV (107–114); V (16–19, 38–61); VI (28–37); VII (61–67, 78–83); VIII (67–71); IX (72–77); X (84–91, 159–161); XI (92–98); XII (109, 115); XIII (115–116); XIV (117–119); XV (119–120); XVI (120–122); XVII (122–123); XVIII (124–126); XX (127); XXI (127–129); XXII (129–132); XXIII (135); XXIV (132–135); XXV (135–136); XXVI (137–143); XXVII (150–151); XXVIII (146–149); XXIX (152–156); XXX (156–159, 161, 162); XXXI (99–106); XXXII (163–169).

Transeau, Sampson, & Tiffany, *Textbook of Botany,* 1953, Harper.
I (1–3); II (7–10); III (61–64, 111); IV (69–70); V (172–176); VII (11–19); VIII through X (61–67); XI (72–76); XII (72–76); XIII (67–69); XIV (67–69); XV and XVI (72–74); XVII (73–76); XIX (75, 79); XX (76–77); XXII and XXIII (20–25, 80–83); XXIV (68–69); XXV (55–58); XXVI (38–43); XXVII and XXVIII (44–60); XXIX and XXX (28–37); XXXI, XXXII, and XXXIII (84–94); XXXIV (94–98); XXXV (42–43, 59–60); XXXVI, XXXVII, and XXXVIII (99–106); XXXIX (99, 165); XLI and XLIII (124–126); XLIV and XLV (127–136); XLVI and XLVII (115–123); XLVIII (137–143); XLIX (144–156); L (107–114, 157–162); LII (165–169); LIII (170–176).

QUICK REFERENCE TABLE TO STANDARD TEXTBOOKS

All numbers refer to pages.

Chapter in this Outline	Topic	Coulter & Dittmer (1)	Emerson (2)	Fuller Plant World (3)	Fuller & Tippo (4)
I	Study of Botany	1–3	1–9	1–6	3–17
II	Plants and Animals		10–11	6–8	18–30
III	Kinds of Plants	11–14	4–6	8–17, 32–36	31–40, 61–65
IV	Cells, Tissues	4–6, 65–69	12–20, 140–141	37–52	66–87
V	Cell Physiology	4–6, 73–77	14–15, 73–77	53–73	88–121
VI	Roots and Soils	11–12, 56–71	78–97	74–99	122–162
VII	Stems: External	11–12, 40–42	98–103	100–115	189–209
VIII	Stems: Internal	42–55	104–109	116–152	210–244
IX	Stem Physiology	40–55	109–122, 137–140	153–172	262–291
X	The Leaf	11–12, 15–39	21–38, 66–72	173–207	292–339
XI	Metabolism	51–52, 19–39	39–65	208–232	340–378
XII	Growth and Responses	72–83	123–135	233–258	379–427

Chapter	Topic	(1)	(2)	(3)	(4)
XIII	Flowers	255–275	314–328	259–289	428–474
XIV	Fruits and Seeds	276–287	319–331	18–31, 290–301	41–60, 475–485
XV	Heredity	288–296	151–162	302–324	486–520
XVI	Classification	84–91	182–186	325–334	521–532
XVII	Algae	92–133	187–191, 201–228	335–362	533–607
XVIII	Fungi	134–182	192–199, 229–263	363–416	608–708
XIX	Bryophyta	201–212, 234–238	264–275	417–432	709–736
XX	Psilopsida	213–275, 224–225	276–278	433–438	737–750
XXI	Lycopsida	212–215, 219–224	281–287	439–448	751–771
XXII	Sphenopsida	224–228	279–280	449–454	772–781
XXIII	Pteropsida	229–254	288–314, 330–337	455–483	782–843
XXIV	Evolution	297–310	163–181, 336	484–504	845–886
XXV	Ecology	288–296	337–386	505–534	887–933
XXVI	Plants in Human Life			535–550	935–948

QUICK REFERENCE TABLE TO STANDARD TEXTBOOKS

All numbers refer to pages.

Chapter in this Outline	Topic	(5) Haupt	(6) Hill et al.	(7) Northen	(8) Robbins, Weier, & Stocking	(9) Sinnott & Wilson	(10) Smith et al.	(11) Taylor & Weber	(12) Transeau et al.	(13) Weatherwax	(14) Wilson & Loomis
I	Study of Botany	3, 5-7	3-4	8-16	1-12	1-16	1-3	1-5	1-9		3-4, 9-12
II	Plants and Animals	3-5		5-8		1-2					24-25
III	Kinds of Plants	10-16	4-9	21-32	13-18 33-37 45-49	17-29	4-9	40-46	10-25	5-9	13-19 22-38
IV	Cells, Tissues	17-30	10-18 19-38	45-66	50-61 96-104	31-44	10-25	17-25 47-56	59-67	14-19 146-157	39-54
V	Cell Physiology	22-25	121-132 201-206	67-73 236-240	61-80	51-57 134-138	26-45	25-39	195-220 447	19-29 185-189	55-64
VI	Roots and Soils	42-60	99-120 129-136	133-173	136-153 172-177 193-198	45-60	46-80	77-97	294-332	97-122	22 37-38 143-154
VII	Stems: External	61-79	139-119	175-190	91-128	81-87	81-82 115-132	56-57 75-76	215-261	124-126 134-139 170-177	22-30 34-37
VIII	Stems: Internal	80-95	149-188	191-209	91-128	87-109	82-115	56-74	262-293	125-133 147-150	102-131
IX	Stem Physiology	95-97	188-199	210-217	133-135 184-193 199-200	75	108-210 214-223	118-120	232-233 242-244 268-269	161-168	139-142 192-204
X	The Leaf	98-114	39-75 82-91	100-131	154-171 188-191 202-213	61-80	133-154 176-190	98-118	26-39 68-94 101-128	69-76 139-143 215-216	65-80 132-142
XI	Metabolism	114-133	76-98 303-324	74-99 219-232	72-75 177-183 214-218	111-132	154-205	121-137	95-100 129-189	31-40 78-95 179-182 41-44 46-67	80-101

See pages vi-vii for list of complete titles.

Practical Hints

For effective use of this Outline or of any supplementary text, good study habits are necessary. The following suggestions will prove helpful. First, the student should read each topic very slowly in his textbook and then study the same topic in the Outline. Second, he should go back to the textbook and make written notes on the significant principles and facts. Third, he may derive great benefit from writing a summary of his own and comparing it with the Outline's treatment of the topic. His summary should include all new terms and names together with definitions or identifications. Finally, for each group of related topics, he should periodically review his lecture notes, laboratory reports, textbook assignments, and pertinent chapters in the Outline.

The following companion books in the College Outline Series are especially recommended for the student's basic library:

> General Anthropology
> General Biology
> First Year College Chemistry
> Physics
> Physics without Mathematics
> General Zoology

The student is urged to make full use of the two types of cross references featured in this and other books of the College Outline Series. This system of cross references correlates topics in standard textbooks with the same topics in the Outline. When studying an assigned textbook, the reader should consult pp. vii-ix, the "Tabulated Bibliography," which will help him readily locate the pages of the Outline that correspond to the assigned chapters of his textbook. When using the Outline as a syllabus or overview, he should consult the "Quick Reference Table to Standard Textbooks," which serves as a guide to detailed treatments of each topic.

Many additional suggestions concerning methods of study may be found in *Best Methods of Study* in the College Outline Series.

Table of Contents

CHAPTER I

THE STUDY OF BOTANY

DEFINITION

Botany is the branch of biology which deals with the structure, physiology, reproduction, evolution, diseases, economic uses, and other features of plants. The word botany is traceable to ancient Greek words meaning "graze," "plants," and "cattle."

HISTORY OF BOTANY

Ancient Period. Greek scientists laid the foundations of botanical study. They studied plants especially in relation to their uses as food and as sources of drugs. They also discovered many facts concerning the growth, distribution, and cultivation of plants The Romans showed little interest in plants, aside from their use as drug and food plants.

Medieval Period. During the Middle Ages, most botanical study was carried on in monasteries and in the botanical gardens associated with universities. This study was often a mixture of scientific observations upon plant structure and behavior, with accounts of the superstitions about and the mythology of plants. Emphasis was placed upon the study of edible and medicinal plants and frequently upon descriptions of the forms of plants. The chief botanical books, called Herbals, of the Medieval Period frequently contained drawings or wood-cut illustrations of the plants described. Attempts at the classification of plants were made during this period.

Modern Period. The modern scientific study of the facts of plant life, divorced from superstition and mythology, began in the late seventeenth and early eighteenth centuries. Outstanding among the botanists of the early modern period was Swedish Carolus Linnaeus (1707-1778), who established many of the fundamental principles of scientific plant classification and named many species of plants. The study of classification and of gross structure were the earliest branches of botany to develop, for they required no specialized tools or techniques from other sciences. The study of the minute anatomy and the functional phases of plant life developed later, following the discovery of the basic principles of chemistry and physics and the perfection of magnifying lenses. Most of the details of the microscopic structure of plants and of the physiological activities of plants have been worked out within the past hundred years.

During the early part of the modern period, the study of crops, gardening, and many other very practical phases of plant study were considered as fields of botany. These fields have grown so enormously, however, that they are now considered as separate sciences, though they are closely related to the study of botany, as the word is now used. Among these daughter-sciences of botany are *agronomy,* the science of field crop-production, *horticulture,* the science of greenhouse, garden, and orchard plants, *bacteriology,* the study of bacteria, *forestry,* the science of the forest, and others.

The term "botany" in its modern sense is regarded as the study of plants for the direct interest which they hold for the human mind, without any compulsion to consider practical aspects of plant life. The science of botany consists of several fairly distinct, though closely related branches:

1. PLANT MORPHOLOGY, the study of plant structure.
2. PLANT ANATOMY, a phase of morphology dealing with the minute internal structure of plants, with reference to tissues.
3. PLANT TAXONOMY, the study of plant classification, and the principles of plant classification and identification.
4. PLANT PATHOLOGY, the study of the causes, control, and other features of plant diseases.
5. PLANT PHYSIOLOGY, the study of the chemical and physical processes and behavior of plants.
6. PLANT ECOLOGY, the study of plants in relation to their environment.

7. PLANT GEOGRAPHY, a phase of plant ecology, dealing with the distribution of plants on the earth's surface.

8. PLANT GENETICS, the study of inheritance and the breeding of plants.

9. PLANT CYTOLOGY, the study of the structure and physiology of individual cells, especially in relation to genetics.

REASONS FOR STUDYING BOTANY

An Asset in a Liberal Education. Since education consists essentially in the achievement of advantageous adjustment to one's environment and since plants constitute one of the most conspicuous features of human surroundings, a knowledge of the fundamental principles which govern plant life is an important part of a liberal education.

An Appreciation of the Place of Human Beings in Nature. An awareness of man's complete dependence upon plants for food, textiles, rubber, dyes, lumber, and many other products increases man's appreciation of the activities of plants and of his place in nature.

An Important Tool in Many Professions. In many practical fields, such as forestry, pharmaceutics, agronomy, horticulture, plant breeding, soil conservation, and bacteriology, a knowledge of the fundamental features of plant behavior is essential or exceedingly helpful.

CHAPTER II

THE LIVING STATE; PLANTS AND ANIMALS

THE NATURE OF LIFE

Life is a series of complex phenomena exhibited by living organisms. The characteristic features which distinguish living organisms from non-living entities are:

1. THE POWER OF ASSIMILATION, or the conversion of non-living materials into living substance (*protoplasm*).

2. IRRITABILITY, or the ability to perceive happenings in the environment and to react to them.

3. THE POWER OF REPRODUCTION OF SIMILAR OFFSPRING.

4. THE POWER OF DECOMPOSING CERTAIN ORGANIC SUBSTANCES, known as foods, with the release of energy which is used in the performance of various physiological processes.

5. CELLULAR ORGANIZATION. See page 11.

THE EXPLANATION OF LIFE

Two schools of thought attempt to explain the nature of life:

The Mechanistic Philosophy holds that all of the activities of living organisms can be explained in terms of chemical and physical reactions. The practice of most scientific biological research is based upon the mechanistic explanation of life and thus makes use of the tools of chemistry and physics. However, many biologists, though their investigations are based on mechanistic assumptions, are aware that the fundamental nature of life has never been explained and that the vitalistic philosophy must therefore be regarded with respect.

The Vitalistic Philosophy holds that not all activities of organisms are explainable in terms of chemistry and physics, but

4

that there is in all living organisms a mysterious vital force which cannot be measured or analyzed by any of the methods of modern science.

THE ORIGIN OF LIFE

Several theories have attempted to explain the origin of life on the earth's surface:

The Theory of Divine Creation, which assumes that life was created by an act of a Divine Creator.

The Inter-planetary Theory, which holds that the first life to appear on the surface of the earth reached the earth from some other planet.

The Theory of Spontaneous Generation, which holds that life arose — and possibly still arises — directly from non-living matter.

The Biogenic Theory, which states that all living organisms develop from other living organisms.

The inter-planetary theory is not regarded seriously by modern biologists. The theory of spontaneous generation seems to have been disproved by the work of Pasteur and others. The theory of Divine creation is based upon faith. The biogenic theory does not explain the first appearance of life on the earth, but merely states that all life comes from preëxisting life. Thus, no completely satisfactory explanation of the origin of life has ever been devised.

PLANTS AND ANIMALS

Living organisms are separated into two groups, plants and animals. There are no differences which distinguish all plants from all animals. The differences which distinguish most plants from most animals are these:

1. Most plants are able to manufacture their own food from raw materials from the air and soil, while all animals lack this ability and depend upon plants for their food.

2. Most plants possess the green pigment, *chlorophyll*, which is lacking in animals.

3. Most plants contain cellulose in their structural frameworks, a substance lacking in all but a few species of animals.

4. Most plants are stationary, whereas most animals are capable of locomotion.

5. Most plants have an unlimited scheme of growth, as contrasted with the limited scheme of most animals. In unlimited growth, there are *meristems* (growth zones) which persist during the life of the plant and add to its size.

The fact that there is not a single difference which separates all plants from all animals is important evidence for the idea that plants and animals are very closely related and have a common ancestry. In some very primitive organisms, there are mixtures of plant and animal characteristics, so that it is often impossible to classify them as either plants or animals.

CHAPTER III

THE KINDS OF PLANTS;
THE STRUCTURE OF SEED PLANTS

THE KINDS OF PLANTS

There are about 350,000 known species of plants. These vary in their structure, methods of reproduction, habits of growth, size, physiological activities, rate of growth, longevity, and environmental preferences.

Plants are classified on the basis of their structural and reproductive differences, chiefly the latter, which vary less than the former under varying environmental factors. Different botanists classify plants differently, for opinions vary as to the true relationships among plants. There are two common usages in classification, one *natural,* expressing insofar as it is possible the true relationships among plants; and the other *artificial,* providing a quick, efficient method of identifying plants. The modern trend in classification is to emphasize *natural* systems, try to perfect them, and utilize the *artificial* approach merely for convenience.

The plant kingdom is usually divided into the two subkingdoms, *Thallophyta* and *Embryophyta.*

Thallophyta. These are the simplest and most primitive of all plants; they are principally water plants but include some land plants which are parasites and saprophytes. They do not form embryos, that is, the young offspring remaining for a time within a parent structure. The Thallophyta consist of various *phyla,* seven of which contain plants that have chlorophyll and manufacture their own food. These seven phyla often are collectively designated as *algae.* Three other phyla of the Thallophyta lack chlorophyll and include parasitic and saprophytic plants known

7

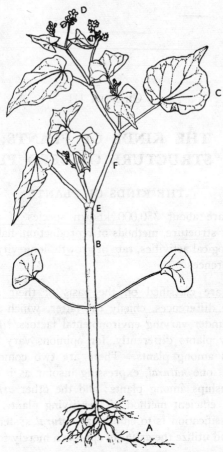

Fig. 1. Seed plant (Buckwheat). A. Roots.
B. Stem. C. Leaf. D. Flower. E. Node.
F. Internode.

collectively as *fungi*. The Thallophyta number about 110,000 species, of which about 90,000 species are classified as fungi.

Embryophyta. These constitute a more advanced group and are chiefly land plants. They form embryos, which for at least a brief time are held within some structure of the parent plant and in this way receive protection and food from the parent. Most species of Embryophyta contain vascular, or conducting, tissues. The Embryophyta, which number about 240,000 species, are separated into two phyla. These are *Bryophyta* (mosses and their relatives), which lack vascular tissues and number about 23,000 species; and *Tracheophyta*, which possess vascular tissues and number about 217,000 species. Included in the phylum Tracheophyta are two classes of seed plants: *Gymnospermae* (cone-bearing plants such as pines, firs, spruces, and cedars); and *Angiospermae* (true flowering plants such as roses, geraniums, corn, apples, and lilies). Gymnospermae and Angiospermae are called "seed plants" because they produce seeds. Seed plants form the dominant part of the vegetation of the earth's land masses.

THE STRUCTURE OF SEED PLANTS

The bodies (Fig. 1) of typical seed plants are made up of four kinds of parts: *roots, stems, leaves,* and *cones or flowers.* Roots, stems, and leaves are *vegetative* parts concerned chiefly with securing raw materials, the manufacture, transportation, and utilization of food, and processes of growth. Cones and flowers are the *reproductive* parts; they are not involved in the elaboration of food, but serve primarily for the production of seeds, the characteristic reproductive structures of seed plants.

Roots normally grow beneath the surface of the soil. The functions of roots are:

1) The absorption of water and dissolved materials (chiefly mineral salts) from the soil.

2) The anchorage of the plant.

3) The conduction of water and dissolved substances from the root up into the stem and of foods from the stem down into the root.

4) The storage of food.

Stems normally grow above the ground, as aerial continuations of the root system. The primary functions of stems are:

1) The conduction of materials from roots to leaves and from leaves to roots.

2) The storage of foods and other substances.

3) The production and support of leaves and flowers or cones.

Leaves are usually bifacially flattened, occasionally, needle- or scale-like appendages of stems. Their chief function is the manufacture of foods from water and mineral salts absorbed from the soil and from the carbon dioxide of the air. A leaf consists usually of a stalk (*petiole*) and a flattened blade.

A stem with its leaves and branches is called a *shoot*.

Cones and flowers are highly modified reproductive shoots which bear specialized organs (cone scales, stamens, etc.) concerned with the formation of seeds.

CHAPTER IV

THE MICROSCOPIC STRUCTURE OF PLANTS; THE STRUCTURE OF PLANT CELLS; TISSUES

HISTORY OF CELL STUDY

In their work on plants, botanists were limited to study of gross morphology until the development of magnifying lenses. Robert Hooke, an English scientist, in 1665 examined a thin slice of cork under a microscope and found it to be composed of tiny compartments which he termed _cells_. In 1675 an Italian physician, Malpighi, published an account of the microscopic, internal structure of plants. Other botanists and zoologists continued the work of examining the cellular structure of plants and animals. Several of these investigators found in the box-like cells of plant and animal bodies a rather viscous liquid which was termed _protoplasm_ by von Mohl in 1846. This substance was recognized as the actual living matter of cells. In 1838, Schleiden and Schwann, botanist and zoologist respectively, set forth the _Cell Theory,_ which states that the bodies of all plants and animals are composed of structural units termed cells, that plants and animals develop as a result of the formation of new cells, and that the activities of an organism are a summation of the activities of its component cells. This theory summarized a growing biological conviction—namely, that the box-like cells with their living bits of protoplasm were the units of which the bodies of all plants and animals are made. This theory has dominated most fields of biological thought until the present time.

About 1885-1895 another theory of the organization of living beings, termed the _Organismal Theory,_ was proposed. This maintains that a living organism is to be regarded, not as an aggregation

11

of individual cells, but as a single functional unit, subdivided for physiological and structural convenience, into small masses of protoplasm, which, with their surrounding walls or membranes, are called cells. The Organismal Theory, which has become increasingly accepted, emphasizes the idea of a coördinated whole, made up of structural units which coöperate in their functions and their development.

An organism which consists of a single cell is termed a *unicellular organism*. Often a number of similar, unicellular organisms become grouped together without any division of labor; these aggregations are termed *colonies*. A *multicellular* organism is composed of many cells among which there are structural and functional differences.

Within the past 75 years, the knowledge of cell structure and of the microscopic anatomy of plants and animals has become a large and important field of biology. The branch of biology which deals with the structure and physiology of cells is called *cytology*.

CELL SIZE

Most plant cells are so small that they can be seen clearly only with the aid of a compound, high-magnification microscope. The diameters of most plant cells lie between .1 and .01 millimeter (1/250 and 1/2500 inch). Certain kinds of cells are larger or smaller than these dimensions; some bacterial cells are only 1/50,000 of an inch long, whereas fibre cells in the nettle family commonly attain a length of eight inches. Such dimensions, however, are extremes.

The extremely small size of plant cells is illustrated by the fact that a single, full-grown apple leaf contains about 50,000,000 cells.

CELL STRUCTURE

A typical plant cell (Fig. 2) consists of three major portions:

(1) The Cell Wall.

(2) **Protoplasm,** the living part of the cell, enclosed by the cell wall.

(3) **Inclusions,** non-living structures present in protoplasm.

The Cell Wall. The cell wall gives support and form to the cell and to the plant as a whole, and protects the protoplasm within. The cell wall consists of several layers, the central one of which is called the *middle lamella,* or *intercellular layer.* This thin layer is composed chiefly of sticky, gelatinous materials known as *pectic substances;* these form a mucilaginous layer which aids in holding the other wall layers together. Outside the middle lamella are other wall layers, composed chiefly of *cellulose,* a carbohydrate which is tough, strong, and elastic and which is the most abundant constituent of the cell walls of most plants. In addition to cellulose and pectic substances, cell walls contain minerals, often waxy substances (e.g., *suberin* in cork-cell walls), *lignin* (a tough material associated with cellulose particularly in wood cells), oils, resins, etc. These substances are mainly products secreted by the living protoplasm inside the wall and are non-living. Cell walls do not dissolve in water, but are capable of absorbing and holding water in large quantities.

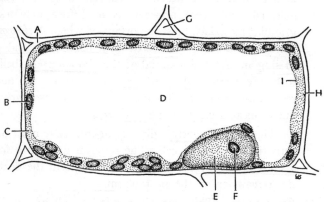

Fig. 2. Green plant cell. A. Cell wall. B. Chloroplast. C. Cytoplasm. D. Vacuole. E. Nucleus with chromatin. F. Nucleolus. G. Intercellular space. H. Cytoplasmic membrane. I. Vacuolar membrane.

Cell walls are not always continuous but frequently possess thin areas (pits) and perforations. Through the perforations, strands of protoplasm extend from one cell to another, facilitating the transfer of materials and irritable impulses. Through the pits, water and dissolved substances diffuse from one cell to another.

Protoplasm. Protoplasm is the living substance of cells. It is a more or less transparent liquid which is somewhat slimy and mucilaginous in texture. Its viscosity varies from that of thin syrup to that of nearly-solidified gelatine. It may be colorless or contain various pigments. Protoplasm is not homogeneous but consists of a variety of structures which can be seen with microscopic examination. These structures are classified into *nucleus* and *cytoplasm*.

(1) NUCLEUS. The nucleus is a usually spherical or ovoid, rather dense, viscous portion of the protoplasm. There is usually one nucleus per cell, although some kinds of cells contain several to many nuclei; there are also a few kinds of cells in which no visible nuclei are present. The nucleus appears as a clear globule in a living cell, but upon the addition of certain dyes is seen to consist of several parts: a thin *nuclear membrane* which separates the nucleus from other parts of the protoplasm, a small spherical *nucleolus* (sometimes more than one), the exact function of which is not known, but which is believed to contain reserve material, and what appears as a diffuse network of granular materials, most important of which is *chromatin*, which is intimately connected with inheritance and comprising an essential material of the *chromosomes*, believed to be the carriers of hereditary traits. Inside the nuclear membrane and surrounding the nuclear network and nucleolus is a clear, liquid *nuclear sap*.

The nucleus controls directly or indirectly most of the activities of a living cell. The removal or destruction of a nucleus usually results in a short time in the death of the remainder of the protoplasm.

(2.) CYTOPLASM. This term is applied to all of the living substance outside of the nucleus. The cytoplasm, like the nucleus, is not uniform in appearance but contains several types of structures. Most important of these are the *cytoplasmic membranes, plastids*, and *mitochondria*.

There is a *cytoplasmic membrane* on the surface of the cytoplasm, just inside the cell wall; this membrane is important in controlling the entry and exit of materials from the cytoplasm within.

Plastids are commonly ovoid or spherical in form, less frequently of some other shape. These are not present in all cells, but are common in leaf cells and in storage cells of roots, tubers, etc. There are three types of plastids. The green plastids, or [1] *chloroplasts,* contain a green pigment *chlorophyll* and, in lesser quantities, two yellowish pigments, *xanthophyll* and *carotene.* Chloroplasts are the food-making structures of protoplasm. The colorless[2] *leucoplasts* build up sugars into starch grains; they are abundant in roots, tubers, and other storage organs.[3] *Chromoplasts* are red, yellow, or orange and are common in certain fruits (tomatoes), flower petals (nasturtiums), and roots (carrots); they contain xanthophyll and carotene and their exact function is not known. In some cases, a single plastid may pass through all three types in succession, beginning as a leucoplast and becoming finally a chromoplast.

Mitochondria are granular or rod-shaped bodies, which are centers of production of regulatory chemicals which participate in respiration and may be related to other physiological processes.

Inclusions. These non-living bodies are chiefly waste-products or foods which may be converted into living protoplasm. Among the common types of inclusions are *starch grains, oil drops, protein bodies, crystals,* and *vacuoles.* A vacuole, usually in the central part of a mature cell, is a watery solution of sugars, salts, and various other substances. Less frequently vacuoles contain oil. Vacuoles are important as storage reservoirs and as partial regulators of the entry and exit of various materials from cells. Each vacuole is surrounded by a *vacuolar membrane* similar to the membrane on the surface of the cytoplasm.

TISSUES

Cells vary greatly in size, structure, and functions. Their differences in structure reflect the different functions which they perform in the life of a plant. A group of structurally similar cells performing the same function is called a *tissue.* An *organ* (e.g., a leaf or a stem) is a major portion of a plant body and is composed of various kinds of tissues. The various plant tissues (Fig. 3) are classified on the basis of their structural and physiological differences, as follows:

(1) Embryonic (Meristematic) Tissues.

(2) Permanent Tissues.

1) SIMPLE PERMANENT TISSUES.

    a. *Epidermis.*

    b. *Parenchyma.*

    c. *Sclerenchyma.*

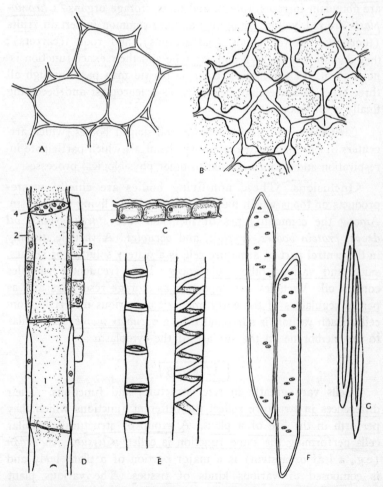

Fig. 3. Plant tissues. A. Parenchyma. B. Collenchyma. C. Epidermal cells with cutin. D. Phloem: 1 sieve tube; 2 companion cell; 3. parenchyma; 4. sieve plate. E. Xylem vessels—annular and spiral. F. Tracheids. G. Xylem fiber cells.

    d. *Collenchyma.*

    e. *Cork.*

2) COMPLEX PERMANENT TISSUES.

    a. *Xylem.*

    b. *Phloem.*

(1) **Meristematic Tissues.** These are located at the tips of roots and stems, between the water- and food-conducting tissues of stems, and at various other places in plant bodies. Meristematic cells are small, thin-walled, frequently cubical, densely packed with protoplasm, and capable of producing new cells by *cell-division.* These new cells by processes of growth and differentiation become the *permanent tissues* of the plant. Permanent tissues do not become changed into other kinds of tissues as do meristematic tissues.

Permanent Tissues.

(1.) SIMPLE PERMANENT TISSUES. Each tissue composed of similar cells.

    a.) *Epidermis.* The epidermis is a tissue which forms a covering layer over leaves, the softer portions of stems and roots, etc. It is usually one cell thick and often has a waxy substance (*cutin*) deposited on its walls. It functions primarily to protect the inner tissues against excessive evaporation of water, and, in roots, to absorb materials from the soil. The epidermis of leaves and often stems contains pores (*stomata*), through which exchange of gases may occur. Epidermal cells are usually colorless, with the exception of *guard cells,* which are green. Guard cells occur in pairs, each of which encloses a stoma.

    b.) *Parenchyma.* This common tissue is composed of thin-walled, large-vacuoled, usually spherical, cylindrical, or ovoid cells. These cells frequently contain chloroplasts and thus manufacture food. Non-green parenchyma cells function chiefly for food- and water-storage.

c.) *Sclerenchyma.* Composed of thick-walled, strengthening cells of two kinds: elongated, tapering *fiber cells* and shorter *stone cells.* Full-grown sclerenchyma cells are dead. Both are common strengthening tissues of stems. Stone cells are common in walnut shells, the skin of pears, bark, etc.

d.) *Collenchyma.* Composed of thick-walled, strengthening cells which remain alive longer than sclerenchyma cells and which are characterized by thickened corners. Common in stems.

e.) *Cork.* Composed of cells which die soon after they are formed and which have walls waterproofed by *suberin.* Protect inner tissues against excessive evaporation. In tree-bark, potato skins, etc.

(2.) COMPLEX PERMANENT TISSUES. Each tissue composed of more than one kind of cell.

a.) *Xylem.* Conducts water and dissolved substances chiefly upward through roots, stems, leaves, and flower stalks. The kinds of cells commonly found in xylem are: *tracheids, vessels, fibers,* and *parenchyma.* Tracheids are elongated, tapering cells which are dead at maturity and which serve for strength and conduction; their walls are usually pitted. Vessels are not single cells but are long, continuous tubes formed by the dissolution of the end walls of vertically-elongated cells; vessels serve chiefly for conduction. Xylem fibers are elongated, pointed strengthening cells with much thickened cell walls; at maturity they contain no protoplasm. They differ from tracheids chiefly in their thicker walls and reduced pits. Xylem parenchyma cells are storage cells. In some plants, the xylem lacks one or more of these kinds of cells.

b.) *Phloem.* Conducts chiefly foods, principally downward from leaves into stems and roots. Composed of *sieve tubes, companion cells, fibers,* and *paren-chyma.* Sieve tubes are vertically-elongated rows of cylindrical cells with perforated end-walls and cytoplasm; these are the chief conducting cells of the phloem. Companion cells border the sieve tubes and seem to aid the latter in conduction. Phloem fibers are thick-walled, elongated strengthening cells. Phloem parenchyma cells are storage cells.

CHAPTER V

THE PHYSIOLOGY OF PLANT CELLS

PHYSICO-CHEMICAL NATURE OF PROTOPLASM

Protoplasm is not a true solution, but is chiefly a *colloidal system.* In a colloidal system, the particles present are not individual molecules or ions as in a true solution, but are aggregations of molecules suspended in some medium; in protoplasm, these particles are suspended in water. Because of their complexity, their frequent instability, their powers of surface attraction, their ability to absorb and hold large amounts of water, etc., colloidal systems allow many varied chemical and physical reactions to proceed at the same time in the same *protoplast* (protoplasm of a single cell).

The chemical elements found in living protoplasm are found likewise in non-living materials. There is no chemical element found exclusively in living protoplasm. The most common and most abundant elements in plant protoplasm are *carbon, oxygen, hydrogen,* and *nitrogen.* Present in smaller quantities are *sulfur, phosphorus, iron, calcium, potassium, magnesium,* and often other minerals, such as *aluminum, copper, sodium, boron, zinc,* etc.

These usually do not occur in protoplasm as elements, but are combined into chemical compounds. *Water* is most abundant of these compounds, frequently constituting more than 90 per cent of protoplasm. Of the solid materials, *proteins* are the most important and largest constituent compounds of protoplasm. Proteins are nitrogenous foods. Also found in living protoplasm are *sugars, oils, fats, pigments, organic acids,* etc.; these are mainly not parts of the living protoplasm itself but are the fuel, lubrication, and waste products of the protoplasmic machine.

DIFFUSION

Cause — molecular motion
Direction of — concentration

① **Simple Diffusion**

1) gas into air (mixture of gases)
     a. CO_2 & O_2 into & out of plant
     b. H_2O vapor out of plant (transpiration)

2) <u>solid into liquid</u>
     a. sugar throughout plant
     b. mineral salts into roots

② **Imbibition**

1) <u>liquid into solid</u>
     (result — solid swells)
     a. liquid H_2O into cell wall
     b.   "   "   "   starch grains.

③ **Osmosis**

1. liquid through a <u>differentially</u>
     <u>permeable membrane</u>
     Results in osmotic pressure &
       turgidity
     a. liquid H_2O thru cytoplasmic
     membrane into vacuole.

Each thing diffuses independently
    depending on its own concentration

<u>liquid</u> water only thing that
    passes thru a plant by osmosis

<u>transpiration</u> — loss of water from
    a plant in the form of
    vapor

The individual chemical compounds of protoplasm cannot be designated as living or non-living. It is the complex system of these chemical compounds which is alive.

DIFFUSION AND OSMOSIS

Water is absorbed in large quantities by plant cells and is important in plants because:

1) It is a constituent of living protoplasm.
2) It is a raw material used in food manufacture.
3) It is the medium of absorption and of transportation of solid materials in plants.
4) It is the medium in which most of the chemical reactions in protoplasm take place.
5) It provides the pressure which is necessary for the maintenance of form, for support, and for growth.

Water is absorbed by plant cells by:

Imbibition. The absorption of water by dry or partly dry colloidal materials, as, for example, the absorption of water by cotton, by a sponge, by a blotter, etc. Cell walls and protoplasm absorb water by imbibition. Cell walls of most plant cells are *freely permeable*—they permit the passage of water and dissolved materials.

moves into cell walls & causes swelling

Osmosis. The diffusion of a liquid (water, in living organisms) through a *differentially permeable membrane* (a membrane which allows certain substances to pass through it, but which restricts or prevents the passage of other substances). Osmosis depends upon (1) Diffusion. (2) Differences in concentration of the diffusing substance. (3) A differentially permeable membrane. (4) The nature and concentration of dissolved materials not able to pass through the membrane.

1. Diffusion is the tendency of a substance to spread out from the place of its greater abundance (concentration) to a place of its lesser abundance (concentration). Gases diffuse (e.g., ether from an open bottle), liquids diffuse (e.g., alcohol diffusing in water), solids diffuse (e.g., sugar diffusing in a cup of coffee).

2. The direction of diffusion depends upon the concentrations of the diffusing substance in different places, a substance normally diffusing from the place of its greater to that of its lesser concentration. The chief tendency in diffusion is toward equalization of concentrations. Rate of diffusion depends on difference in concentrations, temperature, and other factors.

3. A parchment membrane is differentially permeable, permitting water to pass through but not cane sugar. If the large end of a funnel is covered with a parchment membrane, if the funnel is filled with sugar solution, and if the funnel is placed with its large end down, just beneath the surface of pure water in a bowl, osmosis occurs. There is relatively more water in the bowl outside the funnel than in the solution in the funnel, as a consequence of which water moves into the funnel from the bowl through the membrane, in accordance with the diffusion-tendency to equalize concentrations of water on both sides of the membrane. The only manner in which this tendency can be satisfied is by the passage of water into the funnel; equalization of concentration of the two solutions cannot be achieved by the diffusion of sugar out of the funnel into the bowl, since the membrane is impermeable to sugar. In this experiment water accumulates in the funnel and if the small, open neck of the funnel is stoppered, the water begins to exert a pressure, called *turgor pressure*.

4. The greater the concentration of dissolved particles to which a membrane is impermeable, the smaller is the relative concentration of water in which these particles is dissolved. In the experiment above, the greater the number of sugar particles in the water inside the funnel, the smaller is the relative concentration of water molecules in the funnel and the greater the difference between the concentrations of water inside the funnel and in the bowl outside the funnel. Thus, the kind and number of dissolved particles to which a membrane is impermeable

influence the relative concentrations of the liquid in which they are dissolved, on both sides of the membrane, and hence influence osmosis.

Active Water Absorption. Recent research indicates that imbibation and osmosis alone cannot explain all water absorption by plant cells. *Active water absorption* appears to be related to energy released in respiration.

ABSORPTION OF WATER BY LIVING CELLS

A plant cell, such as a root epidermal cell, is similar to the experiment described above. The vacuole with its cell-sap is a water solution of sugars, salts, and other substances, comparable with the sugar solution in the funnel. Between the cell wall and the vacuole are the cytoplasmic and vacuolar membranes, comparable with the parchment membrane. Outside the root cell is the *soil solution* (water with small concentrations of salts and other dissolved materials), comparable with the pure water in the bowl. The cytoplasmic membranes are differentially permeable— they allow water to pass through freely but they restrict the passage of sugars and certain other dissolved substances in the cell-sap. Because of the large numbers of dissolved particles of such substances in the cell-sap, there is relatively less water in the cell-sap than there is in the soil solution, as a result of which water moves by osmosis into the protoplasm from the soil solution. Water moves from cell to cell in large part as a result of differences in water concentrations (or stated conversely, differences in concentrations of dissolved substances) in different cells. The term *osmotic concentration* refers to the relative amount of dissolved materials to which the cell membranes are impermeable or nearly so. The direction of water movement is from cells of low osmotic concentration to cells of high osmotic concentration. *Osmotic pressure* is the maximum pressure which can develop in a solution separated from pure water by a rigid membrane permeable only to water. The *turgor pressure* which develops in a cell as a result of entry of water is usually less than the theoretical osmotic pressure which could develop in that cell, because cell membranes are not rigid and are permeable to substances other than water.

PLASMOLYSIS

Water continues to enter a plant cell so long as the concentration of water in a solution outside the cell exceeds that inside the cell. If the concentration of water in a solution outside a cell becomes less than that inside, water diffuses out of the cell in accordance with the laws of diffusion. This outward diffusion of water causes a shrinkage of the protoplasm away from the cell wall, a condition known as *plasmolysis.* Plasmolysis occurs when salt is placed about the roots of a plant or when a piece of plant tissue is placed in a salt solution. The presence of large amounts of salt results in a decrease in the relative concentration of water outside the cells, as a result of which outward diffusion of water and plasmolysis occur. Plasmolysis is involved in the killing of weeds by placing salt about their roots, and in the preserving of meats and jellies by the addition of salt and sugar respectively. The spoilage of such foods is caused by living bacteria and molds present in the air. Falling upon salted meat or upon sugared jellies and preserves, these bacteria and molds are plasmolyzed and thus spoilage is averted. The addition of excessive amounts of fertilizer salts to soils often causes plasmolysis. If plasmolysis continues too long, the death of the plasmolyzed cell results.

THE ABSORPTION OF SOLUTES

The absorption of dissolved materials (*solutes*) by living cells is a very complex phenomenon not completely explained. One of the controlling factors in this process is diffusion. In *passive absorption,* solutes follow the fundamental law of diffusion—namely, they move from regions where they are more abundant (e.g., soil) to regions where they are less abundant (e.g., root cells). Often, however, the movement of solutes into plant cells is contrary to this law of diffusion (*active absorption*). The phenomenon of active absorption, which proceeds contrary to the laws of simple diffusion, has not been completely explained; certain colloidal phenomena are involved and metabolic activities involving the expenditure of energy are important in bringing about active absorption. Only substances dissolved in water can enter or leave protoplasm. In most cases, the absorption of a single kind of substance is independent of the absorption of other solutes, each solute behaving independently, diffusing as described above from high to low concentration, or frequently from low concentration of the solute to high in active absorption.

The principal solutes absorbed by plants from the soil are mineral salts: sulfates, nitrates, phosphates, etc. The various soil solutes taken up by roots from the soil are absorbed chiefly in *ionic* form, rather than *molecular* form. These ions usually do not accumulate in root cells but move to other cells where they are used up in food manufacture and other processes. Thus, there are frequently smaller concentrations of these ions in roots than there are in the soil and these ions may pass into root cells in accordance with the fundamental laws of diffusion.

METABOLIC PROCESSES OF PLANT CELLS

The term *metabolism* is applied to the sum total of chemical changes involved in the physiology of plants. Among the most important metabolic processes of plants are:

Photosynthesis. The manufacture of carbohydrate food from carbon dioxide and water in the presence of light and chlorophyll.

Respiration. The oxidation of foods to release the stored energy in foods and make it available for growth, protoplasm-building, movement, etc.

Assimilation. The conversion of foods (chiefly proteins) into living protoplasm.

Digestion. The conversion of complex foods into simpler foods.

Food Storage. The conversion of sugars to starch, of glycerol and fatty acids to fats, etc.

Fat and Protein-Synthesis. These foods are elaborated from carbohydrates, mineral salts, etc.

THE FORMATION OF NEW CELLS

Growth by the formation of new cells is characteristic of living organisms. This process, known as *cell division,* is a resultant of various metabolic processes, such as food synthesis, respiration, etc. Cell division in higher plants occurs chiefly in buds on stems, in root tips, in the *cambium* (a growing tissue between wood and bark), and in several other places.

The formation of new cells involves two processes:

(1) **Mitosis**, division of the cell nucleus into two nuclei.

(2) CELL WALL FORMATION between the two nuclei formed by mitosis, producing two new cells.

Mitosis. Mitosis occurs in several fairly distinct phases (Fig. 4), as follows:

(1) PROPHASE. The scattered chromatin of the nucleus condenses into rod-shaped bodies called *chromosomes*. The number of chromosomes is usually constant in body cells of all organisms of the same species. The nuclear membrane

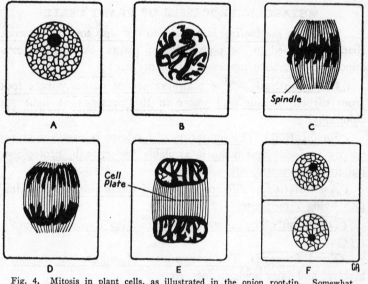

Fig. 4. Mitosis in plant cells, as illustrated in the onion root-tip. Somewhat diagrammatic. A. Growing or "resting" cell. B. Prophase—formation of chromosomes. C. Metaphase—division of the chromosomes on the equator of the spindle. D. Anaphase—migration of the chromosomes toward the poles. E. Telophase—organization of the daughter nuclei. The cell plate is beginning to form. F. The two daughter cells in the growing stage.*

disappears and simultaneously a *spindle* forms in the cytoplasm. This is made up of fiber-like strands, the spindle fibers. The chromosomes become arranged in the central portion of the spindle. The nucleolus disappears.

(2) METAPHASE. Each chromosome splits lengthwise to form two daughter chromosomes, qualitatively and quantitatively like each other.

---

* Reprinted by permission from *An Outline of General Biology*, by Gordon Alexander, published by Barnes & Noble, Inc.

3. ANAPHASE. One of each pair of daughter chromosomes passes along a spindle fiber toward one end of the spindle, the other daughter chromosome of the same pair moves along a fiber toward the opposite end of the spindle. Thus, in the anaphase there are two complete sets of daughter chromosomes, one set moving in one direction, the other in the opposite direction.

4. TELOPHASE. The two sets of daughter chromosomes reach opposite ends of the spindle. The chromosomes in each set by diffusion and branching re-form the diffuse chromatin network of the nucleus. Thickenings appear on the spindle fibers across the central region of the spindle; these constitute the *cell plate,* which results, after several transformations, in a new wall across the cell, separating the two daughter nuclei. The spindle fibers disappear and the nuclear membranes and nucleoli reappear. The process of mitosis is completed in approximately 45 minutes to one hour.

The fundamental biological significance of the complex process of mitosis lies in the fact that it brings about an absolutely equal division of the hereditary substance, *chromatin,* between the two daughter cells formed from a parent cell. This equal division of hereditary substance occurs in every mitosis, so that every daughter cell formed as a result of mitosis has exactly the same amount and kind of chromatin as the parent cell which produced them. Since this chromatin is organized into chromosomes, it follows that every such daughter cell has the same number of chromosomes and the same kinds of chromosomes. In other words, the chromosomes maintain their number and identity from cell to cell.

CHAPTER VI

ROOTS AND THEIR RELATION
TO SOILS

Plants are in close contact with the soil through their root systems. Most roots grow beneath the surface of the soil. The chief functions of roots are:

1) Anchorage of the plant in the soil.

2) Absorption of water and dissolved minerals from the soil.

3) Conduction of water and minerals upward into stem.

4) Conduction of foods manufactured in leaves downward to growth and storage-regions of roots.

5) Food storage.

SOILS

Soils vary in their origin, chemical nature, physical properties, depth, etc. Most soils consist of (1) air, (2) water, (3) rock particles, (4) mineral salts and other soluble inorganic chemical compounds, (5) organic matter, and (6) living organisms.

Air Content of soils is important to plants because oxygen is necessary for respiration. In clay soils there is more air than in loam and sandy soils, which consist of larger particles and have less air space. If spaces among soil particles become filled with water (waterlogged), air is forced out, a condition which may cause injury to plants if it persists. Plowing separates soil particles and results in better aeration.

Water Content of soils is determined by rainfall, drainage, water holding power of soil particles, nature of subsoil, etc. Water which flows away from surface of soil is called *run-off* *water. Gravitational water* is that which percolates down through soil to the standing water (*water table*) below the soil surface. *Capillary water* is held loosely by soil particles. It is chiefly capillary water which is available to the roots of plants. *Hygroscopic water* is that which is held tenaciously by soil particles after they have given up their capillary water. Hygroscopic water cannot readily be removed from soil particles by roots and thus is of little importance to plants. As certain parts of the soil dry out, water may move into the dry portions by capillary movement from moister parts of the soil. This capillary movement of water is important in that it often causes the rise of water from the standing water to the upper layers of soil when the latter begin to dry out. If soil particles are tightly packed, capillary movement is more rapid than when they are loosely packed. Thus, evaporation of water from the soil can be checked by plowing, which prevents packing of particles. This is the basic principle of *dry farming.* Another method of reducing evaporation of water from soil is *mulching,* the spreading on the soil of a layer of material, such as straw, dead leaves, paper, etc., which screens soil from wind and sun and thus reduces evaporation. Another advantage of plowing and mulching is the reduction of weed growth. Clay soils hold water very tenaciously.

Rock Particles vary in size from the microscopic particles of clay to large sand and gravel particles. Rock particles originate from the decomposition of rock by the action of water, freezing and thawing, winds, glaciers, etc.

Mineral Salts, chiefly nitrates, sulfates, and phosphates, are important raw materials used by plants in the manufacture of foods and other organic materials. These substances develop partly from the disintegration of rock particles, partly from the decay of organic matter in the soil.

Organic Matter is derived from the waste products and decomposing remains of plants and animals. Much of this material is derived from the dead roots, leaves, and stems of plants. The term *humus* is applied to the partly-decayed, dark-colored organic residue of soil. Organic matter is important in that it promotes retention of water, prevents caking, increases porosity and aeration, and restores, as a result of its disintegration by bacteria, molds, and other soil organisms, to the soil and air the inorganic mineral salts and gases absorbed and used by green plants in food manufacture. Organic matter is thus important in soil fertility. The addition of manure and the plowing-under of certain plants, such as alfalfa, increases the organic matter of soils. Organic matter promotes growth of soil organisms.

Organisms of many kinds, such as bacteria, molds, algae, insects, worms, etc., live in the soil and may be considered as a part of the soil. Their waste products and dead bodies enrich the organic matter of soils, they aid in the decomposition of organic matter and rock particles, and they influence the physical properties and aeration of soils by stirring up the soil particles.

THE INFLUENCE OF PLANTS ON SOILS

Plants influence soils in three general ways:

(1) They absorb materials (chiefly water and mineral salts) from soils. If the fertility of soils is to be maintained, these mineral salts must be frequently restored by the addition of fertilizers, for the harvesting of fruits, leaves, roots, and other products of plants depletes the mineral content of soils. Soils may be fertilized by the addition of mineral salts, manure, dead plant bodies, such as decayed leaves, straw, etc. Crop rotation (the planting of different kinds of crops in different years) aids in preventing too rapid loss of fertility, for different crops absorb mineral salts in different quantities and thus do not exhaust the soil of any one or several minerals as rapidly as the repeated growth of a single kind of crop.

(2) Plants add materials to soils. The death and decay of plants add to the organic matter of soils. Further, the roots of living plants excrete certain materials into the soil. Chief among these is carbon dioxide, which with water forms carbonic acid, a substance which attacks and disintegrates certain types of rock particles. The roots of some plants apparently excrete certain

waste organic products into the soil. Some of these may be toxic to the plants which produce them or to other plants.

(3.) The much-branched root systems of plants aid in holding soil and thus reduce or prevent soil erosion. Also, plants break the force of falling rain and thus reduce its washing action on soil. Grasses are most effective of all plants in binding the soil and preventing erosion.

THE ORIGIN OF ROOTS

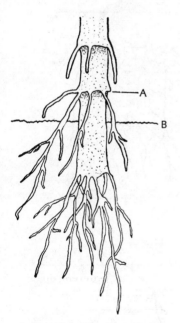

Fig. 5. Adventitious roots of corn. A. Node. B. Soil surface.

A seed contains a tiny plant, the *embryo*, a portion of which is the *hypocotyl*. This structure or a portion of it becomes the first root (*primary root*) of a plant. As it grows, the primary root produces branches, termed *secondary roots*. A primary root usually grows vertically downward, with its secondary roots in somewhat horizontal position. Sometimes roots arise from stems, leaves, or other parts of plants; such roots, which develop from structures other than a hypocotyl or a primary root, are called *adventitious roots* (Fig. 5). The prop roots of corn, the aerial roots of ivy, and the roots formed on stem and leaf cuttings are adventitious.

THE GROSS STRUCTURE OF ROOTS

The term *root system* is applied to the entire mass of underground roots produced by a plant. The extent, form, depth, and other features of root systems vary in different species of plants and under different conditions of growth.

Two common types of root systems (Fig. 6) are *diffuse (fibrous) root systems,* and *tap-root systems.* In a diffuse root system there are several to numerous main roots, usually slender, of about the same size, with numerous smaller root branches. Corn, wheat, and other grasses have diffuse, slender roots. Sweet potatoes and dahlias have diffuse roots, the larger of which become swollen by the storage of food. In a tap-root system there is a main primary root which is conspicuously longer and usually thicker than all other roots of the system. Beets, carrots, and dandelions have tap-root systems.

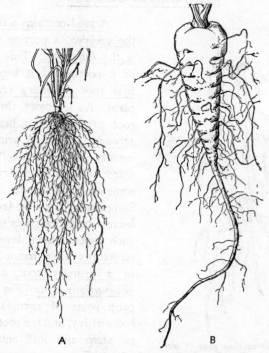

Fig. 6. Root systems. A. Diffuse root system (rye).
B. Tap-root system (carrot).

Root systems often exceed stem systems in their length, degree of branching, etc. Alfalfa roots are sometimes 40 feet in length, those of sugar beets 5 feet, those of black locusts 50 feet. In a full-grown rye plant, the total length of roots of all sizes may reach 380 miles, with a surface area of over 2500 square feet.

Roots are usually cylindrical in form and are usually color-less, or have some color other than green. Roots lack *nodes* ("joints") and *internodes* (distances between successive nodes). Roots lack buds, leaves, and flowers. The branches of roots originate from an internal tissue (pericycle) of the root; they do not arise externally (from buds) as do the branches of stems. Young roots bear root hairs, fragile projections from the epidermal cells of the roots; these hairs appear white and cottony to the naked eye. They increase greatly the absorptive surface of the root. It has been estimated that the root hairs of a rye plant have a total length of about 6600 miles. The root hairs do not grow at the very tip of a root. This region is covered by the *root cap,* a thimble-shaped mass of cells which covers the *embryonic* tissue and thus protects it from injury from soil particles.

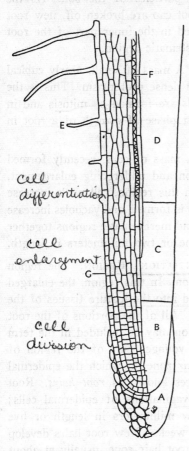

cell differentiation

cell enlargement

cell division

Fig. 7. Longitudinal section of young root. A. Root cap. B. Meristematic region. C. Elongation region. D. Maturation region. E. Root hair. F. Stele. G. Epidermis.

THE MICROSCOPIC STRUCTURE OF ROOTS

A knowledge of the internal anatomy of roots is obtained from the examination of (1) a longitudinal section of a root, (2) a cross section of a root.

Longitudinal Section of a Young Root (Fig. 7). In such a section, four cell regions of somewhat different aspect are visible:

(1.) ROOT CAP. A thimble-shaped mass of moderate-sized cells forming the apex of the root and protecting the *meristematic* (dividing) cells just above it. The outer cells of the root cap are continually being broken off by their contact with rock particles of the soil. As the outermost cells of the root cap are broken off, new root cap cells are being formed in the inner part of the root cap by cells of the meristematic region.

(2.) MERISTEMATIC REGION. A mass of small, nearly cubical cells with thin walls and dense protoplasm. This is the region in which new cells are formed by mitosis and in which, therefore, the first phase of growth of a root in length is brought about.

(3.) ELONGATION REGION. A mass of cells, recently formed in the meristematic region and undergoing enlargement, particularly in length. In this region, cell walls increase in length, new protoplasm is formed, and vacuoles increase in size. The elongation and meristematic regions together usually do not exceed one or two millimeters in length.

(4.) MATURATION (DIFFERENTIATION) REGION. The region above the elongation region. In this region, the enlarged cells become differentiated into the mature tissues of the root—xylem, phloem, etc. All of the portions of the root above the elongation region may be included in the term *maturation region*. The younger part of the region of maturation is the *root hair* zone, in which the epidermal cells develop protuberances known as *root hairs*. Root hairs are thus merely evaginations of epidermal cells; they rarely exceed a few millimeters in length or live more than a few days or weeks. New root hairs develop at the lower end of the root hair zone, usually at about the same rate as older root hairs die at the upper limit of the root hair zone. Root hairs become entwined among and closely appressed to soil particles. If a plant is pulled up by the roots, most of the root hairs are broken off by the soil particles. Most of the materials absorbed by roots are absorbed by the root hairs, which may increase the absorptive surface up to 20 times.

Cross-Section of a Root Through the Region of Maturation (Fig. 8). In such a section the following tissues are visible:

(1) EPIDERMIS. The surface layer of cells, which absorb water and dissolved materials from the soil and which offer some protection to the inner tissues of the root.

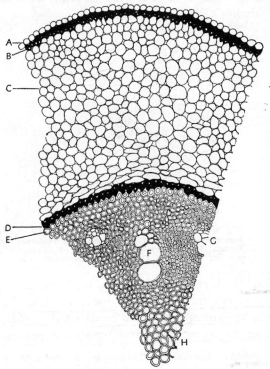

Fig. 8.   Cross-section of a young root (*Smilax*).   A. Epidermis. B. Hypodermis. C. Cortex. D. Endodermis. E. Pericycle. F. Xylem. G. Phloem. H. Parenchyma tissue.

(2) CORTEX. A region of somewhat irregularly-shaped parenchyma cells, with many intercellular spaces. The cortex is chiefly a water- and food-storage region. The innermost cell-layer of the cortex is the *endodermis,* which usually has its inner and side (radial) walls thickened

with *suberin,* a waterproof material. The endodermis apparently functions as a water dam which prevents the outward passage of water from tissues inside the endodermis. The endodermis is believed by some to play a part in the development of root pressure.

(3.) PERICYCLE. A layer of cells inside the endodermis. By cell division, the pericycle gives rise to branch roots, which force their way out through the cortex and epidermis (Fig. 9).

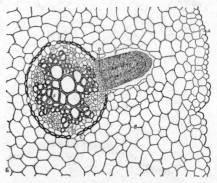

Fig. 9. Cross-section of young root in region of maturation, showing origin of branch root. A. Epidermis. B. Cortex. C. Endodermis. D. Pericycle. E. Branch root. F. Xylem. G. Phloem. H. Parenchyma cells.

(4) XYLEM. Composed of vessels, tracheids, etc. Conducts water, minerals, and often foods upward. The xylem cells are arranged in radial bands which extend outward from the center of the root toward the pericycle.

(5.) PHLOEM. Composed mainly of sieve-tubes and companion cells in groups which alternate with the radial xylem bands. The phloem functions chiefly for the downward conduction of food.

(6.) PARENCHYMA. Surrounding the bands of xylem cells and the phloem cells are parenchyma cells which store food and give support to these other tissues.

The term *stele* is applied to the collective pericycle, xylem, and phloem tissues.

As roots grow older, there often develops a *cambium* between the xylem and phloem areas. This becomes a rather irregular circle of meristematic cells which by periclinal cell division produce *secondary* xylem and phloem and thus increase the diameter of the root.

THE PHYSIOLOGY OF ROOTS (SUMMARY)

1) Absorption of materials occurs by osmosis, imbibition, diffusion of solutes, and active absorption.

2) These materials then pass by from the root hairs through the cortex, endodermis, and pericycle into the xylem cells, which conduct these materials upward.

3) Storage of food and water occurs chiefly in the cortex cells of roots and to a lesser extent in the parenchyma cells of the stele.

4) Growth in length occurs in the tips of roots, in diameter in the cambium between the xylem and phloem.

5) Reproduction is brought about in some plants by adventitious buds formed on roots.

6) Roots give off waste products into the soil.

SPECIALIZED ROOTS

The roots of some plants perform functions other than those typical of most roots or perform only a portion of these functions in specialized degree. Such roots are termed *modified* or *specialized roots,* among the common types of which are:

1. AERIAL ROOTS—e.g., in ivy—give support to the climbing stems, may absorb some moisture.

2. PROP ROOTS of corn and pandanus give support to stems.

3. STORAGE ROOTS of carrots, beets, etc., are enormously swollen with stored food.

4. CONTRACTILE ROOTS of bulbs and other underground stems often contract in growth and pull bulb deeper into soil.

CHAPTER VII

THE GROSS STRUCTURE OF STEMS

THE ORIGIN AND NATURE OF STEMS

The first stem of a seed plant develops from a part of the seed embryo known as the *epicotyl,* which is a continuation of the hypocotyl. The epicotyl is a cylindrical structure with a mass of meristematic cells and often a pair of small leaves at its apex. In some plants only the epicotyl appears above the ground; in other cases the epicotyl together with a part of the hypocotyl emerges above the ground. In the former case, the stem develops entirely from the epicotyl (e.g., in garden peas); in the latter, the stem develops chiefly from the epicotyl, with its lower part originating from the hypocotyl (e.g., in garden beans).

The chief functions of stems are: (1) The conduction of materials. (2) The production and support of leaves and reproductive structures. (3) The storage of food. In some plants, stems have other functions of a more specialized nature.

A stem with its leaves is termed a *shoot*. All the stems, branches, and leaves of a plant constitute its *shoot system*. Most stems grow above ground (*aerial stems*); some grow underground (*subterranean stems*). The aerial stems of most plants are *erect* (e.g., elm); in some plants they are *climbing* (e.g., morning-glories), and in others they are *prostrate* (e.g., cucumbers). Subterranean stems also show a variety of growth habits.

THE EXTERNAL STRUCTURE OF STEMS

Aerial stems are commonly classified into two types: (1) *Herbaceous stems*. (2) *Woody stems*.

38

These types of stems differ chiefly in the following ways:

Herbaceous Stems	Woody Stems
a. Soft and green.	a. Tough and not green.
b. Little growth in diameter.	b. Considerable growth in diameter.
c. Tissues chiefly primary.	c. Tissues chiefly secondary.
d. Chiefly annual.	d. Chiefly perennial.
e. Covered by an epidermis.	e. Covered by corky bark.
f. Buds mostly naked.	f. Buds chiefly covered by scales.

A *tree* is a woody-stemmed plant with a single main stem (trunk). A *shrub* is a woody plant with several stems of about the same size.

An examination of a stem in active, growing condition shows a variety of structures, most common of which are *buds* and *leaves*. Buds are located in the axils of leaves, that is, in the upper angles between the points of juncture of leaves with stems. A bud located at the tip of a stem or twig is a *terminal bud;* a bud located along the side of a stem is termed a *lateral,* or *axillary bud*. Buds sometimes develop in places other than the axils of leaves; such buds are called *adventitious*. The point on a stem from which a leaf or bud grows is called a *node;* the length of stem between two successive nodes is an *internode*.

Buds may be classified in several ways, as follows:

1.) *Terminal* and *axillary buds*.
2.) *Naked buds* (without scales) and *covered buds* (with scales).
3.) *Active buds* and *dormant* (resting) *buds*.
4.) *Flower buds* (produce flowers), *branch* or *leaf buds* (produce leaves), and *mixed buds* (produce both flowers and leaves).
5.) *Alternate buds* (one bud at each node), *opposite buds* (two at each node), *whorled buds* (three or more at each node).

A typical bud consists of a mass of meristematic tissue, which by cell division, enlargement, and maturation results in growth in length of the stem and the production of leaves or flowers. An examination of a longitudinal section of a stem tip shows a meristematic region in the bud, a region of elongation, and a maturation region. These regions usually have a greater longitudinal extent in stems than they do in roots. Terminal buds increase the length of the twigs at whose apices they are situated. Lateral buds usually form branches of the twigs on which they are located, together with leaves or flowers or both. Thus the branches of a stem have an *external* origin, as compared with the internal origin of branch roots. In most leaf buds, there are small lateral protuberances of the meristematic tissue; these protuberances develop with the growth of the bud into leaves. A bud is thus a much shortened twig, with nodes, internodes, and leaf rudiments. In naked buds, the meristematic tissue is uncovered; in covered buds, it is covered by overlapping scales which protect the meristematic tissue against temperature extremes, desiccation, and often against the entry of parasites. These scales are often tough, and thick, and sometimes have waxy or sticky secretions which resist water loss.

In annuals and in woody plants in the tropics, the buds usually grow continually during the life of the plant. In woody plants in temperate zones, the buds grow during a growing season, but remain dormant during a season of low temperature or of scant moisture. A bud grows by the elongation of the internodes which it contains and by the formation of new cells at its apex. In covered buds, the scales bend outward and fall away as the internodes of the bud begin to elongate. As the internodes and tiny leaves of a bud develop, axillary buds are formed in the axils of the newly-formed leaves, and toward the end of the growing season, a new terminal bud is formed. In temperate zone woody plants, these buds, formed in one growing season but destined to remain dormant through a winter before the next growing season, are called *winter buds*. The general form of a shoot system depends upon the position, number, kinds, and degree of activity of its buds.

Herbaceous stems bear relatively few structures besides leaves and buds. There may be present *hairs,* which are outgrowths of epidermal cells, *spines,* which may be modified twigs, leaves, hairs, or stipules.

Woody stems show a greater variety of structures than herbaceous stems particularly during the winter, when they usually drop their leaves. Among the structures, in addition to leaves and buds, on woody twigs (Fig. 10) are:

1.) LENTICELS. Tiny raised pores through which gaseous exchange occurs.

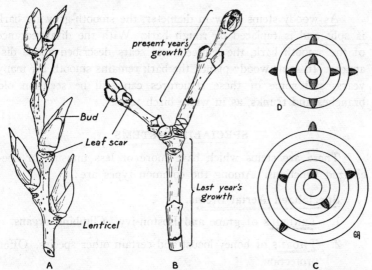

Fig. 10. Winter twigs. A. Cottonwood. B. Box elder. C. Diagram showing the angles between adjacent bud scales, buds, leaves or branches in cottonwood. D. Diagram showing the angles between the same structures in the box elder.*

2) LEAF SCARS. Usually crescent-shaped or circular marks left by the fall of leaves. They are the places at which the leaf stalks grew from the stem.

3) BUNDLE SCARS. Appear as tiny raised dots in the leaf scars. These are the broken ends of *vascular bundles* (conducting strands of xylem and phloem) which extend from the conducting tissues of the twig into the leaf stalk.

4) BUD SCARS. Ring of small narrow scars left by the falling-away of the bud scales and forming a complete thin circle around a twig. Each of these rings of bud-scale scars marks the place at which a terminal bud began its growth. Since a new terminal bud is developed each

* Reprinted by permission from *An Outline of General Biology*, by Gordon Alexander, published by Barnes & Noble, Inc.

year, the number of bud scars on a twig indicates the age of the twig.

5) TWIG SCARS. More or less circular scars left by the falling away of branch twigs, a natural phenomenon in many plants. Similar to twig scars are *fruit scars,* left by the falling away of fruit stalks.

As woody stems grow in diameter, the smooth-growing bark is split and is replaced by rough bark. With the disappearance of the smooth bark, the lenticels and scars described above disappear. In some woody plants, the bark remains smooth for many years, and some of these structures can still be seen on old branches and trunks, as in white birch trees.

SPECIALIZED STEMS

These are stems which have more or less unusual or specialized functions. Among the common types are:

Specialized Aerial Stems.

1. TENDRILS of grape and Boston-ivy. Climbing organs.

2. THORNS of honey locust and certain other species. Offer protection.

3. STORAGE STEMS of cacti. Store food and water.

4. AERIAL BULBS of onions. Serve for reproduction.

5. RUNNERS (STOLONS) of strawberry and other plants. Produce new plants at their nodes when these touch the ground.

Specialized Subterranean Stems.

1. RHIZOMES. A horizontal stem growing at or beneath the surface of the ground. May be slender (quack grass) and serve chiefly for reproduction or may be swollen by stored food (iris). Rhizomes are perennial and send up new shoots year after year from their buds.

2. TUBERS. A tuber (Fig. 11) is an enlarged tip of a rhizome. Stores much food and is located at the end of a slender rhizome (Irish potato). The "eyes" of a

potato are buds which are capable of growing into aerial stems. Pieces of tubers with one or two eyes are used to propagate Irish potatoes.

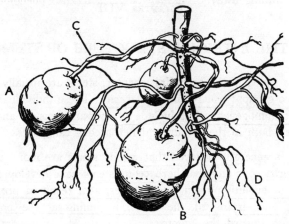

Fig. 11.　Potato tubers.　A. Tuber.　B. Bud.　C. Rhizome.　D. Root.

3. BULBS. A bulb is a large, rather globose perennial bud with a small basal stem at its lower end, from which grow fleshy, scale-like, overlapping leaves. Bulbs serve chiefly for storage, reproduction, and for carrying the plant through seasons unfavorable for active growth. Onion, tulip. *mostly leaves*

4. CORMS. A corm is a rather globose perennial stem with thin, papery leaves on its surface. Most of a corm is stem, in contrast to a bulb, most of which consists of storage leaves. Corms serve for storage, reproduction, and for carrying the plant through an unfavorable season. Gladiolus, crocus.

CHAPTER VIII

THE INTERNAL STRUCTURE OF STEMS

of the same
kind, similar

As stated in the preceding chapter, stems are usually divided into two groups: *woody* and *herbaceous*. These individual groups are not homogeneous but include many variations in anatomical features, both in the woody and herbaceous categories.

It is generally believed that woody stems are more primitive than herbaceous and that herbaceous stems have developed in the course of evolution from woody types, as a result of progressive cooling and drying of the earth, beginning at the poles and extending toward the equator.

THE INTERNAL STRUCTURE AND DEVELOPMENT OF WOODY STEMS

Gross Internal Structure. An examination, with the naked eye, of a cross-section of a woody stem (Fig. 12) shows two major groups of tissues: the *bark,* which forms the outer part of the stem, and the *wood,* or *xylem,* which forms the inner part of the stem. Inside the xylem in some kinds of woody stems a parenchymatous tissue, called *pith,* is present. Between the bark and the wood is the *cambium,* a layer of meristematic cells which by cell division cause an increase in diameter of the stem. In the outer part of the bark there develops a *cork cambium,* which forms *cork cells* in the outer part of the bark. The cambium forms wood cells much more rapidly than it does inner-bark cells; thus, as stems grow older the proportion of wood to bark increases.

Microscopic Internal Structure.

1. PRIMARY TISSUES OF WOODY STEMS. (Fig. 13). *Primary* tissues are those formed by the growth of terminal meri-

stems, which, in stems, are in <u>buds</u>. <u>In woody stems, the primary tissues are formed in the early part of the first season's growth</u> of the twig, but as a twig grows after its first year, the newly-formed tissues are entirely *secondary*—that is, they develop from the cambium and cork cambium. The primary tissues of a woody stem are the *epidermis,* the *cortex,* and the *stelar (fibro-vascular) tissues.*

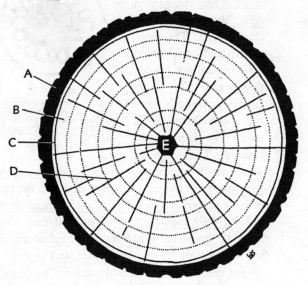

Fig. 12. Cross-section of woody stem. A. Bark. B. Wood, showing annual rings. C. Cambium. D. Vascular ray. E. Pith.

a.   The *epidermis* is <u>a single surface layer of cells, usually with cutinized, nearly waterproof outer walls.</u> The epidermis is a <u>protective tissue</u>, the chief value of which lies in its <u>preventing excessive evaporation</u> from the tissues inside.

b.   The *cortex* varies in thickness in different kinds of stems. It usually contains strengthening *collenchyma* cells, storage *parenchyma* cells, and frequently strengthening *fiber* or *stone* cells. The cortex is thus a region of protection, strength, and storage.

c. The tissues of the *stele* are the *pericycle, phloem, cambium, xylem, rays,* and *pith*. The *pericycle* consists usually of parenchyma cells and often of strengthening fiber cells. These fiber cells in some plants (flax, hemp) are important in the manufacture of thread, twine, and textiles. The *phloem* tissue is just inside the pericycle and consists of sieve tubes, companion cells, fibers, and parenchyma cells. The sieve tubes and companion cells conduct foods downward, the fibers provide strength, and the parenchyma cells store various substances. The *cambium*

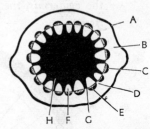

Fig. 13. Primary tissues of woody stem. A. Epidermis. B. Cortex. C. Pericycle fibers. D. Pericycle parenchyma. E. Primary phloem. F. Primary xylem. G. Cambium. H. Pith.

is a usually continuous layer of meristematic cells just inside the phloem. By their division, the cambium cells form new xylem cells inside themselves, new phloem cells outside themselves, and thus cause the stem to grow in diameter. The *xylem* consists of *vessels, xylem fibers, tracheids,* and *xylem parenchyma* cells. The vessels and tracheids serve primarily for conduction, secondarily for support. Xylem fibers are thick-walled strengthening cells. Parenchyma cells store foods and other substances. In the wood (xylem) of some species of plants, one or more kinds of these cells may be absent; for example, the wood of most gymnosperms lacks vessels and xylem fibers. Sometimes other types of cells occur in xylem, e.g., *resin canals* in the wood of certain gymnosperms. A *ray* is a band of cells (chiefly parenchyma) which extends radially in a stem, that is, along a radius of the stem. Rays function chiefly for transverse conduction of materials in stems and for food storage.

The epidermis and cortex are continuous layers of cells forming complete circles in the stem. The primary xylem and primary phloem of some species are likewise continuous layers; in other species, they occur in separate strands, or *vascular bundles*. The cambium of woody stems is usually in the form of a complete circle of cells between the xylem and phloem tissues. In virtually all seed plants the xylem tissue is inside the phloem, with the cambium between xylem and phloem.

2. SECONDARY TISSUES OF WOODY STEMS (Fig. 14).

 a. *The Cambium and Its Derivatives*. After primary tissues of a stem are formed, little or no further growth in length of the particular stem segment

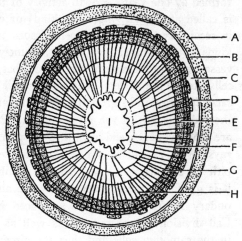

Fig. 14. Cross-section of 3-year old woody stem. A. Cork. B. Cork cambium. C. Cortex. D. Pericycle fibers. E. Secondary phloem. F. Cambium. G. Secondary xylem (3 annual rings). H. Vascular ray. I. Pith.

occurs. These primary tissues of woody stems are formed in the first season's growth. Also, in the first season's existence of a particular stem segment, cambial activity leads to secondary growth. From this time on, all growth in this part of the twig is secondary. Since the cambium is outside the xylem, the secondary xylem cells are produced outside the primary xylem cells, which thus remain the innermost xylem cells of a stem. The most recently-formed xylem cells (secondary xylem) are outermost, just inside the cambium. The new (secondary) phloem cells are produced by the cambium just outside itself; the outermost phloem cells of a stem are primary cells and are thus the oldest of the phloem. In most woody stems, the cambium is active along its entire length, thus forming continuous circular layers of xylem and phloem cells. These continuous circular layers are more noticeable in the xylem than in the phloem, since there is usually more secondary xylem produced than secondary phloem. The layer of xylem formed by one year's growth activity of the cambium is called an *annual ring*. The kinds of cells formed in secondary xylem and phloem tissues are the same kinds found in primary tissues, namely, tracheids, vessels etc., in the xylem, and sieve tubes, companion cells, etc., in the phloem. The cambium likewise forms *secondary rays* in its growth activity and also increases the radial length of the *primary rays*. Primary rays are those which extend inward to the pith. Secondary rays never extend as far toward the center of the pith as the primary rays. As the cambium grows, it is gradually forced outward by the abundant secondary xylem which it has produced inside itself. Cell division occurs radially as well as tangentially in the cambium cells and thus the circumference of the cambium is increased as it is pushed outward by the secondary xylem.

b. *The Cork Cambium and Its Derivatives*. The *cork-cambium* is a secondary meristematic tissue which develops from certain parenchyma cells in the outer part of the cortex. The cork cambium produces cells both on its inner and outer faces, chiefly the latter. The cells formed on the outer face of the cork cambium are *cork cells*. The walls of these cells become *suberized* and thus waterproof and the cork cells die. The accumulated cork cells form the rough, hard outer bark of woody stems; the outer bark reduces evaporation of water from the tissues inside it, protects the inner cells against extremes of temperature, and against mechanical injury. In addition to the cork, cork cambium, pericycle, and cortex, the bark also contains the phloem (inner bark); thus, one of the functions of bark is food conduction. The thickness of bark varies on stems of different ages and in different species of trees. The lenticels in young bark serve for exchange of gases—chiefly the exit of carbon dioxide and the entry of oxygen. As stems grow older, the outer layers of cork are split lengthwise by the more rapidly growing wood within, and the lenticels are no longer apparent.

The Structure of Wood. As stated in the preceding section, wood is xylem tissue and is made up (in angiosperms) of wood fibers, vessels, tracheids, and wood parenchyma. In gymnosperms, the wood is simpler in structure, being composed almost entirely of tracheids. Angiosperm woods are hardwoods, gymnosperm woods are softwoods.

Wood is composed chiefly of *cellulose* and *lignin*, a compound often associated with cellulose. Also in wood are water, dyes, minerals, oils, starch, gums, etc.

In the temperate zones and in parts of the tropics in which there is a definite alternation of growing and dormant seasons, the secondary xylem tissue is produced in layers (*annual rings*) by the cambium. Usually one annual ring is formed each year; thus, the age of a tree or branch may be determined by counting the number of annual rings seen in the cross section. An annual ring (Fig. 15) is composed typically of two somewhat distinct bands of cells; the inner band of each ring is made up of rather large cells formed by the cambium in the spring and hence called *springwood;* the outer band of each ring is made up of smaller, thicker-walled cells, formed in the summer and hence called *summerwood.* The innermost annual ring in a tree is the oldest, the outermost (just inside the cambium) the youngest. The widths of annual rings vary greatly; these variations are reflections of differences in rainfall, soil aeration, and light (chiefly rainfall) which obtained while the ring was being formed. Thus, it is possible to trace climatic cycles by studying the annual rings of trees.

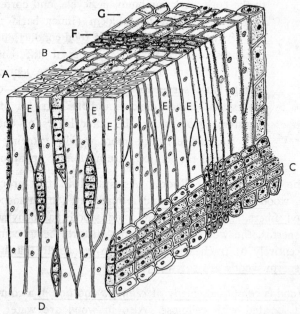

Fig. 15. Pine Wood. A. Summerwood of annual ring. B. Spring-wood of annual ring. C. Side view of vascular ray. D. End (tangential) view of vascular ray. E. Tracheids. F. Cambium. G. Phloem.

Wood sections (Fig. 16) are of three types:

1. Those cut *across* the longitudinal axis of the stem; in such a *transverse, or cross* section, the annual rings appear as concentric circles, with the vascular rays radiating out across the rings, like the spokes of a wheel.

2. Those cut lengthwise through the stem. These are of two types: (a) Those cut tangentially to the annual rings, are at right angles to the radiating vascular rays. In such a *tangential, or slab* section, the annual rings appear to the naked eye as broad, irregular, alternating

light and darker bands, which are the alternating summer and spring wood bands of the annual rings. The cut ends of the vascular rays may be seen as flecks in the annual rings. Tangential sections are the most commonly seen sections in construction lumber. (b) Those cut *radially*, or parallel with the vascular rays. In such a *radial* or *quarter-sawed* section, the annual rings appear as narrow, longitudinal, light and dark bands, with the rays appearing as usually smooth bands running at right angles to the annual rings.

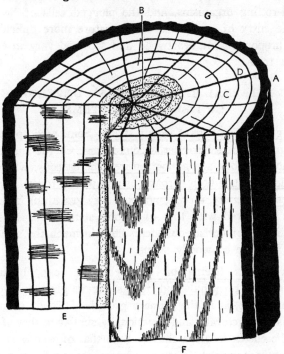

Fig. 16. Three-dimensional view of woody stem. A. Bark. B. Heartwood. C. Sapwood. D. Vascular ray. E. Radial section. F. Tangential section. G. Cross (transverse) section.

As woody stems grow older, physical and chemical changes occur in the wood. The conducting cells of the xylem become plugged up with protrusions of cells (*tyloses*) into their cavities. Also, there is frequently an increase in the amount of *tannins* (bitter substances), *resins, gums,* and *dyes* in wood cells as they grow older. The young annual rings are not plugged and usually have but small amounts of these chemical compounds; these rings conduct actively and have numerous living cells. These rings constitute the _sapwood_ of a tree. The older, plugged rings with larger quantities of tannins, etc., and with no living cells constitute the _heartwood,_ which is usually darker in color than sapwood. The sapwood lies outside the heartwood. The plugged heartwood cells do not conduct materials. Heartwood is much more valuable than sapwood for outdoor construction because it decays much less easily. The resins, tannins, etc., are poisonous or distasteful to wood-rotting organisms, and the plugged cells of heartwood make the entry of organisms and moisture more difficult. The relative proportions of heartwood and sapwood vary in different kinds of trees.

THE INTERNAL STRUCTURE AND DEVELOPMENT OF HERBACEOUS STEMS

All gymnosperms have woody stems. Some angiosperms have woody stems, others have herbaceous stems. Of the angiosperms, the monocotyledons are almost entirely herbaceous, whereas the dicotyledons include both herbaceous and woody forms. In herbaceous stems generally, there is no secondary growth or is relatively little, as compared with that of woody stems. The xylem and phloem tissues of herbaceous stems contain much the same kinds of cells as those of woody stems.

Herbaceous Stems of Dicotyledons (e.g., bean, sunflower). The terminal bud forms, as it grows, epidermis, cortex, and stele, as in the primary growth of woody stems. The epidermis is structurally and functionally similar to that of woody stems; the cortex is often thinner than that of woody stems but is quite similar; the stele is composed of primary phloem, cambium, primary xylem, and pith, as in a young woody twig (Fig. 17).

There is a much larger proportion of pith and cortex as compared with xylem and phloem in herbaceous stems as compared with woody stems. Pericycle fibers are sometimes present. In some plants, the xylem and phloem are in distinct vascular bundles; in others, they are more or less continuous. The vascular bundles in dicots are usually arranged in a single circle.

The cambium is located between the xylem and phloem, with the xylem inside the cambium and the phloem outside. In some species, the cambium occurs only in the vascular bundles, in other species, it is a continuous layer. In either case, the cambium usually shows relatively little activity and there is thus little secondary growth in most herbaceous dicots.

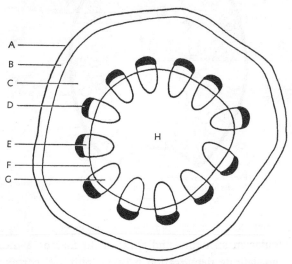

Fig. 17. Cross-section of herbaceous dicot stem. A. Epidermis. B. Sclerenchyma tissue. C. Cortical parenchyma. D. Pericycle fibers. E. Phloem. F. Cambium. G. Xylem. H. Pith.

Herbaceous stems are chiefly annual, but in some cases may live for more than one year, in which case considerable secondary growth occurs and the stem becomes more or less woody.

Herbaceous Stems of Monocotyledons (e.g., corn). Most monocot species (exceptions are palms and a few others) have no cambium and thus no secondary growth. Such stems grow relatively little in diameter; the little diametric growth which does occur results from the enlargement of primary cells.

In all monocots, the xylem and phloem are arranged in vascular bundles, with the xylem in the inner part of the bundle, the phloem toward the outer part. The vascular bundles of monocots are not arranged in a circle as in dicots, but are scattered through the parenchyma tissue which usually fills the stem. The lack of cambium and the scattered bundles are outstanding features of monocot stems (Fig. 18).

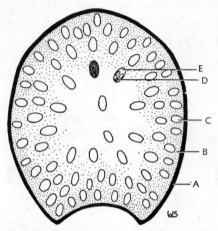

Fig. 18. Cross-section of monocot stem (corn).
A. Epidermis. B. Parenchyma. C. Vascular
bundle. D. Xylem. E. Phloem.

The surface of most monocot stems is covered by an epidermis similar in structure and function to that of a dicot stem. There is no definite demarcation between pith and cortex; parenchyma cells are continuous throughout the stem, surrounding the vascular bundles.

The vascular bundles of monocot stems are surrounded by a layer of thick-walled strengthening cells. Such bundles without cambium, are called *closed bundles,* as compared with the *open bundles* of dicot stems.

Leaf Traces and Leaf Gaps. At each stem node, vascular bundles separate from the xylem and phloem tissues of the stem, pass out through the cortex and enter the leaf-stalk. These vascular bundles are called *leaf traces.* Wherever a leaf trace departs from the vascular tissues of a stem, a small break occurs. Such a break is called a *leaf gap.*

Leaf traces constitute the connections between the veins (vascular tissues) of leaves and the vascular tissues of stems.

CHAPTER IX

THE PHYSIOLOGY OF STEMS

The principal functions of stems are the conduction of materials upwards, downwards, and transversely, and the production and support of leaves and reproductive structures. The production of leaves, internodes, and reproductive structures is the function of buds. The function of support is performed by the strengthening cells which occur in the pericycle, xylem, and phloem, as described in the last chapter.

Other more specialized functions of stems are food storage, climbing, reproduction, water storage, etc., as described in an earlier chapter.

The physiologically most complex function of stems is conduction, or translocation.

CONDUCTION OF MATERIALS BY STEMS

Conduction by Xylem. The chief function of xylem is the upward conduction of water and dissolved substances (*sap*). These dissolved substances are chiefly mineral salts from the soil; also, foods previously stored in the roots and stem may be conducted upward in the xylem, especially in spring in woody plants. Evidences for upward conduction in the xylem are: (1) A ring of bark (of which the phloem is a part) may be removed from a stem, with no interference with the normal condition of the leaves. If the xylem be severed but the phloem left intact, wilting of the leaves follows, for their supply of water and solutes has been shut off. (2) If the cut lower end of a stem is allowed to stand in a water solution of a dye for several minutes or hours and if cross-sections of the stem are then cut and examined, the dye will be found principally in the cells of the xylem. In some plants, there may be a small amount of upward conduction through the phloem.

55

Enormous quantities of water move upward through stems. For example, a single corn plant loses by evaporation about 50 gallons of water during its few weeks of life, a sunflower plant evaporates about 150 pounds of water in its life span of about 140 days. These figures represent only the water which evaporates from plants. In addition, considerable amounts of water and minerals rise to the leaves and are made into foods which remain in the plant.

The exact nature of the forces responsible for the rise of these materials is not known, but several explanations of the *ascent of sap* have been proposed, as follows:

1. ROOT PRESSURE. This is responsible for the exudation of sap from cut stems, as from pruned grapes in early spring. The magnitude of root pressure rarely exceeds two atmospheres, not sufficient to force sap up into tall trees (one atmosphere will push water up only 30 feet). Further, root pressure usually is demonstrable only in early spring before leaves have developed and when upward sap movement is rather slow. During the growing season when leaves are full grown and upward sap movement is most rapid, root pressure is usually nil. Thus, root pressure is probably a negligible factor in sap rise, except possibly for a brief period in early spring and possibly in certain low-growing plants, such as herbs.

2. CAPILLARY ATTRACTION. An example is the rise of liquids in tubes of very small diameter, such as xylem vessels, caused by the attraction of the tube material for the liquid. Capillary attraction never causes a rise of more than a few feet at most, so it is probably a negligible factor in sap rise.

3. ATMOSPHERIC PRESSURE. It has been suggested that atmospheric pressure forces water up through the conducting cells of the xylem, as it supports a mercury column in a barometer. Under ideal conditions, atmospheric pressure could not support a water column higher than 33 feet at sea level. Thus, it is not more than a very minor factor in sap rise.

4. ACTION OF LIVING CELLS. It has been suggested that living cells adjoining the conduction cells of the xylem, force water upward, possibly by some sort of pumping action. However, experiments have shown that dead xylem can conduct sap very readily. Thus, the action of living cells is probably of secondary importance in the rise of sap.

5. IMBIBITION IN CELL WALLS OF XYLEM. The cell walls of xylem cells absorb water by imbibition, but imbibitional force is not sufficient to explain either the rapidity or magnitude of sap rise. Further, the greater part of the sap moves through cell cavities, not cell walls.

6. TRANSPIRATION PULL AND WATER COHESION. *Transpiration* (evaporation) from leaves causes a great water deficit in the leaf cells. As a result of this deficit, water is drawn osmotically from the xylem cells in leaf veins by the cells surrounding the veins. Thus, a pull is exerted in the uppermost xylem cells of plants, those in the leaves. Water molecules have tremendous cohesive power (i.e., they remain together with great mutual attraction), often as much as 150 atmospheres. The pull exerted by the movement of water from the uppermost xylem cells of leaves into the partially dried leaf cells is transmitted through the water columns in the xylem of stems down into the roots. Thus, water is *pulled* up through stems by the evaporation-pull of transpiration and the cohesive power of water molecules. The osmotic pressures in transpiring leaf cells frequently reach 30 atmospheres, more than enough to cause the rise of water to the tops of the highest known trees. (Twenty atmospheres would be sufficient to cause the ascent of sap to the highest known trees.) This attempt to explain sap rise is very generally accepted by botanists at present. It is likely that such factors as imbibition, root pressure, the action of living, cells etc., are contributory factors in sap rise.

Conduction by Phloem. The chief function of phloem is the downward conduction of foods manufactured in the leaves. In some cases, some upward conduction of minerals and foods occurs in the phloem. Evidences for downward conduction of foods in the phloem are:

1. Chemical analyses show the presence of larger amounts of foods in the phloem than in the conducting cells of the xylem.

2. If a complete girdle of bark (including phloem) is removed from the stem, an enlargement develops immediately above the girdle. This swelling is caused by the accumulation of foods above the girdle, since they are unable to pass across the gap and continue their downward journey.

The forces responsible for the passage of foods through the phloem are not well understood. The rate of such movement is usually too rapid to be explained by simple diffusion. The pores in the end walls (*sieve plates*) of sieve tubes facilitate such movement.

Conduction by Vascular Rays. The vascular rays which extend radially in stems extend through xylem and also into the phloem. These rays bring about transverse (crosswise) conduction of foods, mineral, water, and gases. Oxygen entering the lenticels finds its way into the outer ends of vascular rays, some of which terminate just under the lenticels, and is conducted by ray cells into the inner tissues of the stem. Similarly, carbon dioxide is conducted outward to the lenticels from which it passes out into the air.

OTHER FUNCTIONS OF STEMS

Food Storage occurs chiefly in the parenchyma cells of cortex, rays, and pith, and also in the phloem and xylem parenchyma. Water and salt storage also occur in these tissues. In specialized stems, such as tubers, corms, etc., these storage tissues are extensive. Also stored in certain types of stems are *resins, gums, latex* (a milky fluid), etc.

Climbing Stems are tendrils, such as those of grapes, or twining stems, such as those of morning-glories.

Food Manufacture occurs in stems which contain chlorophyll, such as those of most herbaceous plants and of cacti, the stems of which store water and food and manufacture food, in the absence of leaves.

Reproduction is brought about by runners, by the branching of rhizomes, by the formation of new bulbs and corms from older ones, etc.

PRACTICAL APPLICATIONS OF A KNOWLEDGE OF STEM STRUCTURE AND PHYSIOLOGY

A knowledge of the structure and function of stems is fundamental in the horticultural practices of *pruning, girdling,* and *grafting*.

Pruning. In pruning away a diseased, broken, or otherwise undesired branch, the cut should be made as close to the main branch as possible and parallel to it, in order that the growth tissues surrounding the wound may form new tissues to heal the wound. Since the food moving down through the phloem comes from leaves above the wound, the wound must be in a position near this food, if healing is to occur. If the cut is made some distance from the main branch and a stump is thus left, healing of the wound at the end of the stump does not occur because there are no leaves above it—these were removed when the branch, of which the stump is a remnant, was cut off. A pruning wound should be painted to prevent the entry of molds, bacteria, etc., which might cause the wood to rot.

Girdling is the removal of a complete ring of bark (including the phloem). Girdling stops the downward passage of food, which collects above the girdle. Girdling is practiced in order to: (1) Produce large fruits. The accumulation of food causes the fruits above a girdle to become abnormally large. (2) Kill trees, in clearing land. A girdle on the main trunk prevents the downward passage of food and thus starves the roots. (3) Produce more flowers in the following season.

Grafting. Grafting is a horticultural practice in which two freshly-cut stem surfaces are bound together in such fashion that their cells grow together; thus there is formed an organic union between the two pieces of stem. The basal, rooted stem used in a graft is the *stock;* the stem piece which is grafted to the stock is the *scion.* Stock and scions are prepared in various ways which vary according to their size, their internal anatomy, etc. A common type of grafting is *budding,* in which the *scion* consists of a single bud which is placed in a slit in the bark of a young stock.

Precautions necessary to ensure a successful graft are: (1) The stock and scion must be placed together in such a manner that their cambial layers are in contact, for the cambium produces the growth which causes union. (2) Stock and scion must be firmly bound together so that the cut ends of the stem pieces do not move in the wind. (3) The region of the graft should be covered with wax to prevent the entry of parasites into the cut and to prevent the drying out of the exposed tissues. (4) Successful grafts can be made only when stock and scion are very closely related, for only in closely related species are the growth habits and anatomy enough alike to ensure union.

Grafting is employed for several purposes, some of which are: (1) To propagate seedless varieties. (2) To propagate hybrids, the seed of which not all produce offspring of the same kind. (3) To propagate plants the seeds of which germinate poorly. (4) To produce more rapid fruiting. Grafted scions of certain fruit trees produce fruit sooner than saplings raised from seed. (5) To change or fashion the shape of a plant, as in the umbrella catalpa. (6) To check or eliminate parasites which damage the roots of the variety from which the scion is taken but to which the variety of stock on which the scion is grafted is immune. (7) To acclimate certain plants to environments in which their tops grow but which are unfavorable to their roots.

Grafting never produces new kinds of plants. It is exclusively a *vegetative* mode of propagation, and stock and scion always maintain their individualities—there is never any mixing of characters. There are some apple trees in which over a hundred scions have been grafted to the same stock. Each scion continues to produce its own variety of apples.

CHAPTER X

THE LEAF:
STRUCTURE AND PHYSIOLOGY

DEFINITION

A leaf is a lateral outgrowth of a stem, arising at a node, and possessing a bud in its axil. Most leaves are flattened and expanded, but there are modified or specialized kinds of leaves which do not exhibit this flattened structure. The chief function of the common type of foliage leaf is food manufacture.

ORIGIN AND ARRANGEMENT

Leaves develop from the growth (meristematic) tissues of buds. They arise as lateral protuberances of the bud-tip, and as the bud grows and expands, the protuberances enlarge and become differentiated into leaves. There are three common types of leaf arrangement on a stem (Fig. 19).

1. Spiral or alternate, in which there is a single leaf at a node and in which these alternate leaves form a continuous ascending spiral from the basal portion to the apex of the stem. This is the commonest type of leaf arrangement.

Examples: elm, apple, oak.

2. Opposite, in which there are two leaves at a node, usually directly opposite each other (at an angle of 180°).

Examples: ash, maple, buckeye.

3. Whorled, in which three or more leaves grow out from the same node, usually more or less equally spaced. This type of arrangement is least common.

Examples: catalpa, bedstraw.

LONGEVITY OF LEAVES

In most plants, at least of the temperate zones, leaves live for a single growing season, then fall. Such plants are *deciduous*. Plants which retain their leaves for more than one growing season and thus have some living leaves at all times are called *evergreens*. The leaves of most evergreens do not persist more than four years.

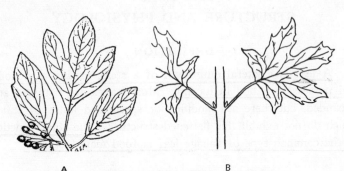

A   B

Fig. 19. Alternate and opposite leaf arrangement. A. Alternate (spiral) arrangement. B. Opposite arrangement.

EXTERNAL STRUCTURE OF A TYPICAL FOLIAGE LEAF

A typical foliage leaf consists of two parts: a stalk, or *petiole*, which grows out from the nodes, and an expanded portion, the *blade*. In many leaves, in addition, small flaps of tissue, the *stipules*, grow out from the base of the petiole at its juncture with the stem. Stipules may be very small and apparently functionless or may be large and leaf-like (Japanese quince) and thus manufacture food. Some leaves lack petioles and consist merely of a blade. Such leaves are termed *sessile*.

The Leaf Blade. The blade is usually flat and thin. Thus light and carbon dioxide, required for food manufacture, penetrate readily all portions of the blade. Leaf blades vary in different plants in size, shape, venation, margin, and number of blades per leaf (Fig. 20).

1. LEAF SIZE. Leaves vary in length from a fraction of an inch *(Elodea)* to ten or fifteen feet (banana, date palm) to fifty or sixty feet (some palms).

<u>2</u>. LEAF SHAPE. Leaf blades vary in shape from *linear* (grass-like) to almost *circular* (nasturtium), with many gradations of form between these extremes.

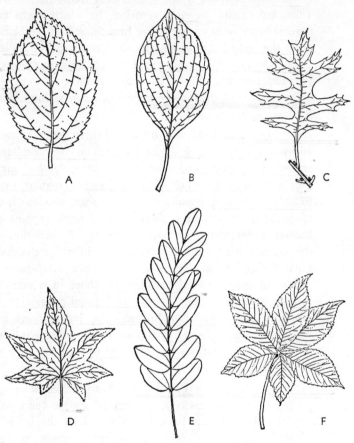

Fig. 20. Leaf shapes and margins. A. Toothed leaf. B. Entire leaf. C. Pinnately-lobed leaf. D. Palmately-lobed leaf. E. Pinnately-compound leaf. F. Palmately-compound leaf.

<u>3</u>. LEAF VENATION. (Arrangement of veins.)

There are two chief types of leaf venation: *parallel* and *net*. In *parallel* venation, the veins run parallel to each other from the base of the blade to the tip (iris, corn), or parallel to each other and at a similar angle to the *midrib* of the blade (banana, canna). In *net* venation, the veins branch out many times and form a complete network over the blade. There are two types of net-veined leaves: *pinnate* venation, in which there is one midrib from which the smaller veins branch out (elm, oak), and *palmate* venation, in which there are several large veins of equal size branching into the blades from the end of the petiole (maple, geranium). Parallel-veined leaves are characteristic of monocotyledons (grasses, cattails, lilies, bananas, orchids, etc.); net-veined leaves of dicotyledons, (roses, oaks, willows, sunflowers, legumes, etc.).

4. LEAF MARGINS. Leaf margins are of three general types: *entire, toothed,* and *lobed. Entire* margins are completely smooth and unindented (dogwood, corn), *toothed* margins are those in which there are rather regular sawtooth indentations, usually not larger than one-fourth of an inch; there may be a single row of teeth (apple) or the larger teeth may be toothed (elm). A variation of the toothed margin is the wave-margin in which the marginal projections are rounded rather than sharp-pointed (chestnut oak). *Lobed* margins are those in which the indentations are large, coarse, and usually variable in size. In *pinnately-lobed* leaves, the indentations are directed toward the midrib (oaks); in *palmately-lobed* leaves, the indentations are directed toward the base of the blade (maples).

5. NUMBER OF BLADES PER LEAF. Most leaves have one blade. Leaves of this type are termed *simple* (elm, oak, apple). Some plants have leaves in which the blade is divided into separate pieces, called *leaflets* (rose, walnut, clover). Such a leaf is termed *compound*. When the leaflets are all attached at the tip of the petiole, the leaf is *palmately* compound (buckeye, clover). If the leaflets are distributed at intervals along the extended petiole, the leaf is said to be *pinnately* compound (walnut, rose).

The Petiole. The petiole is usually cylindrical in form, with vascular bundles running lengthwise through it, connecting the veins of the blade with the xylem and phloem of the stem. In some monocots (grasses), the petiole has the form of a sheath which clasps the stem. Petioles are able to bend in response to the stimuli of light and gravity and thus are able to hold the blade advantageously with reference to the direction of light.

INTERNAL STRUCTURE OF A TYPICAL FOLIAGE LEAF

A cross section of a leaf under the microscope shows three groups of tissues: *epidermis* (lower and upper); *mesophyll,* and *veins* (Figure 21).

Epidermis. This is a single layer of cells forming the upper and lower surface of the leaf. These cells fit tightly together and are of two types: *ordinary* epidermal cells, and green,

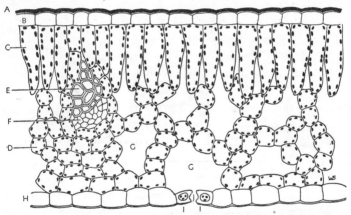

Fig. 21. Cross-section of leaf. A. Cutin layer (cuticle). B. Upper epidermis. C. Palisade tissue of mesophyll. D. Spongy tissue of mesophyll. E. Xylem of vein. F. Phloem of vein. G. Air spaces. H. Lower epidermis. I. Guard cells. J. Stoma.

crescent-shaped *guard cells,* which occur in pairs, with a minute opening, or *stoma,* enclosed by each pair. The ordinary epidermal cells function to protect the inner tissues from dessication, mechanical injury, and to some extent, from the entrance of parasites. These cells often secrete a waxy substance, *cutin,* on their outer surfaces. The cutin layer, or *cuticle,* which is waterproof, varies in thickness in different species and is effective in reducing evaporation.

The *stomata* are avenues of exchange of carbon dioxide and of oxygen and water vapor between the interior of the leaf and the external atmosphere. The opening and closing of the stomata is regulated by changes in the water pressure in the guard cells. This pressure increases when light falls on the guard cells and decreases when darkness comes. Light causes an increase in the sugar content and thus in the osmotic concentration of the guard cells, and water enters, supplying the pressure which expands the guard cells. Light may also have a direct effect on the colloids of the guard cell protoplasm causing them to take up water more rapidly. Thus the stomata are opened widest during the day, closed or nearly closed at night (Figure 22).

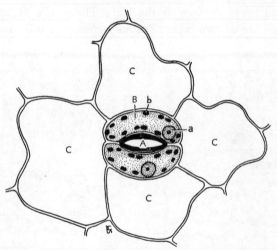

Fig. 22. Guard cells and stoma. A. Stoma. B. Guard cell;
a. nucleus, b. chloroplast. C. Other epidermal cells.

The upper epidermis of most leaves usually has a thicker cuticle and fewer stomata than the lower. Most leaves have between 100 and 350 stomata per sq. mm. of lower surface.

Mesophyll. The mesophyll, occupying the central portion of the leaf, is composed of two distinct tissues: the *palisade* tissue, consisting of vertically elongated, cylindrical cells. Below the one or two *palisade* layers is the *spongy* tissue, composed of loosely-packed cells of variable form. Both layers are rich in chlorophyll and constitute the food-making tissues of the leaf. The numerous intercellular spaces in these tissues make possible the ready diffusion of gases to all cells.

Veins (Vascular Bundles). Veins are branched continuations in the mesophyll of the vascular bundles of the petiole. A vein consists usually of xylem cells (vessels, tracheids) and phloem cells (sieve tubes and companion cells), which conduct respectively water and mineral salts upward into the mesophyll, and foods downward into the petiole. In most leaves, the xylem cells are in the upper part of the veins, the phloem cells on the lower. Larger veins are surrounded by thick-walled strengthening cells which aid in supporting the blade.

PHYSIOLOGY OF LEAVES

Photosynthesis. This process may be defined as the manufacture of carbohydrates from carbon dioxide and water in the presence of light through the mechanism of chlorophyll. It is the basic process of food manufacture in nature and all animals and plants (except a few fungi) depend on it. It is also a major source of oxygen in the air.

Conditions directly necessary for photosynthesis:

(1) Carbon dioxide, which makes up 0.03—0.04% of air and which reaches the interior of the leaf through the stomata and enters the mesophyll cells dissolved in water. Carbon dioxide is said to be the "limiting factor" of photosynthesis since it is the factor present in smallest degree. An increase in the carbon dioxide content of the atmosphere up to .9% increases proportionately the rate of photosynthesis in some plants.

(2.) Water, which is absorbed by the roots and passes through the conducting tissues of the plant to the mesophyll cells.

(3.) Favorable temperature—above freezing, but below 45° C.

(4.) Light. Visible light, especially the red and blue-indigo wave-lengths (those absorbed most readily by chlorophyll), is most effective. This light may be either sunlight or artificial light. About 3% or less of the total energy of sunlight reaching the leaf is actually used in photosynthesis; the remainder is reflected, passes through the leaf, or is absorbed as heat.

(5.) Chlorophyll. This green pigment, which is usually contained in chloroplasts, is the mechanism which is the center of photosynthesis. Its exact manner of operation is not understood. It is constantly synthesized by the leaf in the presence of light and is simultaneously decomposed by light.

Course of the process and products:

Photosynthesis may be represented by the formula: $6 CO_2 + 6 H_2O \rightarrow C_6H_{12}O_6 + 6O_2$. This formula shows merely the raw materials, combining proportions, and products. The intermediate reactions are incompletely known. The oxygen is liberated into the air as a gas through the stomata. The other product, usually glucose (grape sugar), is converted into other materials, such as starch and cellulose, or is used directly as a source of energy, or transported to other parts of the plant or converted into other organic substances (fats, proteins, etc.).

Transpiration. Transpiration is the loss of water vapor from the aerial portions of plants, especially from the leaves. The process is more or less continuous but is much more rapid during the day than at night. *Cuticular* transpiration occurs through cuticle, *stomatal* transpiration through the stomata. Most water is lost in stomatal transpiration.

1. ADVANTAGES AND DISADVANTAGES TO THE PLANT. Transpiration pull is responsible in large part for ascent of sap and in some plants creates a cooling effect within leaves. Its chief disadvantage is that it causes wilting and desiccation if it exceeds water absorption by the roots.

2. FACTORS INFLUENCING TRANSPIRATION. (1) Atmospheric humidity, (2) light intensity, (3) air movement, (4) air temperature, (5) soil conditions.

Low humidity, high air temperature and wind velocity, bright illumination accelerate transpiration. Deficiency of water in the soil reduces rate of transpiration.

3. INTERNAL FACTORS INFLUENCING TRANSPIRATION.

(a) Heavy cutin layers reduce transpiration.

(b) Perpendicular leaves transpire less than those in horizontal position.

(c) Stomata depressed below other epidermal cells transpire less than those exposed to wind.

(d) Reduced leaf surface, shedding leaves in dry seasons reduce transpiration.

(e) Opening and closing of stomata regulate transpiration to some extent but do not constitute a highly efficient control method. Closing occurs usually only after wilting has begun. Stomatal movements serve primarily for oxygen and carbon dioxide exchange, not for transpiration control.

(f) Presence of much colloidal material enables protoplasm to hold water tenaciously. Various gums and related substances are important in this respect.

The amount of water transpired by a plant, divided by its dry weight, is the *water requirement*. This varies in most plants from 200 to 1000. That is, for every pound of dry material manufactured by the plant, 200 to 1000 pounds of water are transpired.

Guttation. Guttation is the exudation of water in liquid form, usually through special pores called *hydathodes*. Guttation occurs usually from well-watered plants on cool, moist nights following warm days. Guttation is probably of little physiological significance.

Leaf-fall and Autumnal Coloration. In autumn, a special layer of cells, the abscission layer, forms at base of petiole. Cells behind this layer become corky and impervious to water, interfering with transportation to leaf and with manufacture of chlorophyll. The normal green color of a leaf is due to the pigment *chlorophyll*. Since chlorophyll is decomposed by light it disappears when the corky layer shuts off the supply of raw materials, allowing other already-present pigments (yellow *xanthophyll* and orange *carotene*) to become evident. Deep red colors are new pigments (anthocyanins) which develop in unknown ways as chlorophyll disappears; deep red colors are associated with high sugar content. Middle wall layers of abscission cells disintegrate, causing cells to separate and petiole to break off at this layer. Cork layer below abscission layer prevents water loss from leaf scar.

Other Physiological Processes of Leaves: Among these are *respiration* (liberation of energy by oxidation of foods), *digestion* (conversion of complex into simpler foods), synthesis of fats and proteins, *assimilation* (incorporation of foods into living protoplasm), and others to be discussed in detail elsewhere.

SPECIALIZED (MODIFIED) LEAVES

In some plants, some or all of the leaves have become modified structurally, so that they resemble little or not at all the typical foliage leaves described above. These structural modifications are correlated with certain specialized functions which these modified leaves perform.

Common types of specialized leaves:

Bud Scales are overlapping, modified leaves which protect the internal growing tissues of the buds of most plants growing in regions of low winter temperatures or great aridity.

Spines with buds in their axils are modified leaves. These may protect the plant from grazing animals.

Bulb Scales of such underground stems as the tulip and onion serve for food storage.

Water Storage Leaves of succulent plants (stonecrop, live-forever), are fleshy, with thick layers of cutin, for the storage of water.

Tendrils of some plants (sweet pea, garden pea) are whole leaves or parts of leaves which are specialized for climbing.

<u>Insect-Trapping Leaves</u> of the pitcher plants, sundew, and Venus' fly-trap are highly specialized for the attraction, capture, and digestion of insects, as a supplement to their normal nutritional requirements.

<u>Reproductive Leaves</u> occur in many groups of plants. Many botanists interpret some of the parts of flowers, pine cones, etc., as leaves which function primarily for reproduction. Foliage leaves of some plants (*Bryophyllum*) are able to produce new plants for their petioles or marginal notches.

Chapter XI

METABOLISM

The term *metabolism* includes all those chemical transformations involved in the physiological and functional processes which take place in the cells of living organisms. Metabolism thus embraces various processes of food manufacture, of food transformations, of the release of the energy stored in foods, of the construction of protoplasm and of cell walls, and of processes of reproduction. The chemical processes of metabolism are numerous and very complex, and detailed knowledge of them presupposes extensive knowledge of chemistry.

FOOD SYNTHESIS

Photosynthesis is the fundamental process of food manufacture. From the sugar made by photosynthesis and from certain mineral salts, all the other kinds of foods in plants are manufactured.

Food. A food is an organic compound from which living organisms derive energy or build protoplasm. All foods contain carbon, hydrogen, and oxygen. These are built into sugars from carbon dioxide and water in photosynthesis. Some foods contain other elements, such as nitrogen, phosphorus, and sulfur. These are obtained from mineral salts (nitrates, phosphates, sulfates) absorbed by roots from soils. Green plants also require magnesium, iron, boron, manganese, potassium, zinc, calcium, and other elements. Not all these elements are built into foods—they may perform regulatory functions. Certain elements are absorbed by plants in considerable quantities and must be restored to soils through fertilizers (made chiefly from bone meal, blood, manure, dead leaves, peat, etc.) to assure continued good growth and yield of crops. Plants can be grown in water solutions of these elements in jars, or in gravel or sand containing water solutions of the elements. The growth of plants in such cultures is called *hydroponics*.

There are three groups of foods: (1) *carbohydrates,* (2) *fats,* (3) *proteins.* Their chemical characteristics and functions follow:

(1.) CARBOHYDRATES. Contain carbon, hydrogen, and oxygen, with the hydrogen and oxygen in the same proportion as they are in water, namely two to one. Some carbohydrates are water-soluble (sugars), others are not (starch and cellulose). The functions of carbohydrates in plants are: [1] to supply energy (sugars), [2] to build cell walls (cellulose), [3] and to build other kinds of foods. Carbohydrates are important energy foods and are stored in many places in plants, chiefly as starches. These are abundant in roots, tubers, fruits, etc. Common carbohydrates are *glucose* ($C_6H_{12}O_6$), *sucrose,* or cane sugar ($C_{12}H_{22}O_{11}$), *starch* [$(C_6H_{10}O_5)n$], and *cellulose* [$(C_6H_{10}O_5)n$].

(2.) FATS AND OILS. Contain carbon, hydrogen, and oxygen, with proportionately less oxygen as compared with the oxygen content of carbohydrates. Fats are manufactured from carbohydrates. Fats and oils are similar chemically, but fats are solids at room temperatures, while oils are liquids. All fats and oils are greasy and are water-insoluble. They occur in all living cells, but are especially abundant in storage organs such as seeds (peanut, soybean), and fruits (banana, avocado). Fats are chiefly reserve foods which can be called upon to supply energy.

(3.) PROTEINS. Contain carbon, hydrogen, oxygen, and nitrogen, and often phosphorus or sulfur or both. Protein molecules are very large and complex. Proteins are the most important substances of which living protoplasm is made and they are thus found in all living cells. They are sometimes used for energy but they are poor in this respect as compared with sugars and fats. Proteins are usually abundant in seeds (beans, corn, peas, etc.); they form the protoplasm of new cells when seeds begin to grow. Proteins are manufactured from carbohydrates, plus minerals. Protein and fat-synthesis can occur in either light or darkness, if sugar is present.

Animals depend on plants for food. They are able to synthesize fats and some proteins from sugars and nitrogenous compounds, but they are unable to make foods from inorganic materials, as plants can.

Methods of Getting Food. *Autotrophic plants* are those which manufacture their own food from inorganic materials. There are two kinds of autotrophic plants: *Photosynthetic,* those which contain chlorophyll and which make food using the energy of light, and *chemosynthetic,* which lack chlorophyll and which obtain their energy for food synthesis by the oxidation of hydrogen sulfide, ammonium compounds, etc. There are several kinds of chemosynthetic bacteria. *Heterotrophic plants* are those which are unable to manufacture their own food and which depend upon previously synthesized foods for their energy and their protoplasm-building. There are two main types of heterotrophic plants: *parasites,* which take their food directly from other living organisms, and *saprophytes,* which get their food from the dead remains or waste products of organisms. Some organisms can live both saprophytically and parasitically. Others (e.g., mistletoe) have some chlorophyll and are thus partly autotrophic, and partly heterotrophic. An example of a parasite is the wheat-rust fungus; of a saprophyte, a mushroom living on dead leaves and other decomposing organic matter in soils.

Other Processes. Plants manufacture other substances besides foods. Among these are chlorophyll, hormones, xanthophyll and other pigments, vitamins, cutin, etc. Many of these substances, such as chlorophyll, have definite functions to perform in connecttion with food manufacture, etc. Others are catalysts, growth-regulators, etc.

DIGESTION AND RESPIRATION

The metabolic processes thus far described are processes of conversion of simple substances into more complex compounds. Proceeding simultaneously with these constructive processes are other metabolic processes which involve transformation of complex organic compounds into simpler substances. Chief among these processes are *digestion* and *respiration.*

Digestion. Digestion is the process in which water-insoluble foods are converted into water-soluble foods, or in which complex foods are converted into simpler, more easily utilized foods. Digestion is necessary before translocation, respiration, and certain other processes can occur.

Digestion involves the uptake of water in transforming complex into simpler foods, as shown by the formula indicating the digestion of maltose (malt sugar):

$$C_{12}H_{22}O_{11} + H_2O \rightarrow 2\ C_6H_{12}O_6$$
$$\text{(maltose)} \quad \text{(water)} \quad \text{(glucose)}$$

Such a process is known chemically as *hydrolysis*. Digestive processes are hydrolytic in nature.

Such a process does not occur spontaneously but requires the action of a digestive agent or catalyst, which initiates and controls the process. The organic catalysts which are produced by protoplasm and which control digestion are termed *enzymes*. The characteristic features of enzymes are:

1. They are not used up or changed in the processes in which they are involved.
2. They are very efficient. A small quantity of enzyme can perform a large amount of work.
3. They are destroyed by heat at or near boiling.
4. They are complex, colloidal materials, probably proteinaceous in nature.
5. They are very specific. Each enzyme digests only a single substance or a few closely related substances.
6. Their action is in most cases reversible; that is, they can build up complex foods from simple foods and vice versa.

Some of the numerous enzymes in plants are:

1. DIASTASE, which converts starch into maltose.
2. LIPASE, which digests fats into *fatty acids* and *glycerol*.
3. INVERTASE, which digests cane sugar into *glucose* and *fructose*.
4. TRYPSIN, which digests certain proteins into simpler nitrogenous compounds.

Respiration. Respiration is the chemical process by which the energy of foods is liberated for use in processes of growth, reproduction, assimilation, movement, etc. Respiration is fundamentally a chemical process of oxidation, or slow combustion. Respiration differs from combustion in that it proceeds slowly under control by enzymes, without the rapid evolution of heat characteristic of combustion. There are two chief types of respiration: *aerobic* and *anaerobic.*

(1) AEROBIC RESPIRATION occurs in the presence of abundant, free, atmospheric oxygen. The substance most commonly oxidized is glucose; less frequently, fats, proteins, and other substances are respired. The most common products are carbon dioxide and water. The equation which represents the common type of aerobic respiration is:

$$C_6H_{12}O_6 + 6\ O_2 \rightarrow 6\ CO_2 + 6\ H_2O + \text{energy}$$

(glucose)   (oxygen)   (carbon   (water)
                               dioxide)

The carbon dioxide may escape into the air through stomata and lenticels or may remain in the plant and be used in photosynthesis. The energy released is frequently in excess of that needed for the processes named above; some energy is radiated from the surface of the plant body as heat, or may produce *luminescence,* or dim light, as in certain fungi.

The chief differences between photosynthesis and aerobic respiration are:

Photosynthesis	Respiration
Absorbs carbon dioxide	Forms carbon dioxide
Forms oxygen	Uses oxygen
Makes sugar	Destroys sugar (and other substances)
Increases weight	Decreases weight
Only in green cells	In all living cells
Only in light.	At all times.

(2) ANAEROBIC RESPIRATION, OR FERMENTATION, occurs in the absence of, or presence of limited quantities of, oxygen. Sugar, proteins, and other substances are re-

spired anaerobically. Processes of anaerobic respiration are enzyme-controlled reactions. One of the common enzymes of this type is *zymase*, which converts glucose into ethyl alcohol and carbon dioxide. The products of fermentation are quite varied; among these are carbon dioxide, alcohol, and others. A common type of anaerobic respiration is the fermentation of sugar and the production of alcohol and carbon dioxide by yeasts, which are one-celled fungi. Another type is the fermentation of alcohol by acetic acid bacteria to acetic acid (vinegar).

Anaerobic respiration is the only method of respiration in many kinds of fungi and as such is their means of getting energy from foods. In higher plants the first stages of respiration, which may occur without oxygen, transform glucose into pyruvic acid; if oxygen is present, respiration is completed aerobically, the pyruvic acid being converted into carbon dioxide and water. If oxygen is absent, anaerobic respiration occurs, the pyruvic acid being broken down into carbon dioxide and alcohol. Although the first phase of respiration in higher plants is anaerobic, these plants cannot long survive if they are deprived of oxygen.

Respiration is affected by a number of external factors, such as temperature, oxygen, the presence of oxidizable substances, carbon dioxide, poisons, etc.

Respiration may be investigated by measuring the heat produced, the oxygen used, and the carbon dioxide produced. Carbon dioxide forms a white precipitate of barium carbonate in barium hydroxide solution, or of calcium carbonate in calcium hydroxide solution.

CHAPTER XII

GROWTH AND RESPONSES

Growth may be regarded as a resultant of the many metabolic processes of plants. Growth involves (1) *the formation of new cells,* (2) *the increase in size of these cells,* (3) and *the maturation (or differentiation) of cells.* Growth thus involves the manufacture of food and other organic substances, assimilation, digestion, respiration, etc. Growth usually results in an irreversible gain in size and weight and a more or less irreversible differentiation of cells, tissues, and organs. If a curve is plotted to indicate the growth in size of an organism at regular intervals, the curve is S-shaped, indicating that growth begins slowly, then passes into a phase of rapid enlargement (*grand period of growth*), following which the growth rate gradually decreases until the point of cessation.

Growth occurs chiefly in buds, root tips, cambium, cork cambium, and root pericycle. In all of these regions, the same series of events occurs: cell formation, enlargement, and differentiation.

A *response* is a movement of a plant part (less frequently, of a whole plant) in reaction to some received stimulus, such as light, moisture, etc. Responses are mechanisms by means of which organisms adjust themselves to their environments and thus increase their chances of survival.

THE FACTORS INFLUENCING GROWTH

Since growth is a resultant of many metabolic processes, it is affected by many *internal* and *external* factors.

(Internal Factors Influencing Growth.) The chief internal factors affecting growth are:

1) AGE. Young organs usually grow more rapidly than older organs.

2.) HEALTH. Healthy organisms grow in more normal fashion than do diseased organisms.

3.) HEREDITARY FACTORS. The growth pattern of a species is determined by its hereditary potentialities. Hereditary factors are important in determining both rate and form of growth. It is only within the limits set by hereditary factors that external influences can affect growth.

4) GROWTH REGULATORS. These are manufactured by living protoplasm and are important internal growth regulators. Among these substances are *auxins* (hormones), which are involved in cell wall elongation, *growth inhibitors,* which seem to control certain growth phases, and *vitamins* which are necessary for the normal growth and development of plants. Growth regulators frequently exert their influences at some distances from their places of origin.

5) NUTRITIONAL RELATION between carbohydrates and nitrogen compounds. An excess of nitrogen seems to promote vegetative growth, while an abundance of carbon promotes reproductive activity. The total amount of stored food available for assimilation and respiration is also important in regulating growth.

External Factors Influencing Growth. The chief external factors which influence growth are:

1) LIGHT. Light is necessary for photosynthesis. It influences rate of growth, auxins, formation of chlorophyll, leaf size, digestion, etc. The daily duration of exposure to light affects reproductive activity (*photoperiodism*). Some plants form flowers only if they are exposed to light less than 13 hours a day, others when the daily exposure is over 13 hours. Plants grown in the dark are spindly, succulent, without chlorophyll, and with undeveloped leaves; this condition is known as *etiolation*.

2.) TEMPERATURE. In most plants, the most favorable temperature for growth is about 75-85° F. Temperatures near freezing and above 120° F. usually result in cessation of growth and often death. Certain plants may be made somewhat resistant to low temperatures by exposing them to gradually decreasing temperatures, a process called *hardening*. Seeds and other dormant structures are less susceptible to temperature extremes than are actively growing plant parts.

3) MOISTURE. A deficiency of water causes stunted growth. Excess moisture may also stunt growth, if it decreases the amount of oxygen in the soil. Photosynthesis, digestion, growth, assimilation, and other metabolic processes require water, either as a raw material, a solvent, a medium of translocation, etc. *Hydrophytes* are plants which grow in water or very wet soil and which have weak stems, little or no cutin, abundant air spaces and which usually lack root hairs. *Xerophytes* grow in arid or semi-arid soils and have thick cutin layers, abundant storage tissues, much-reduced leaves. *Mesophytes* grow in moderately moist soils; most of the plants in the United States are mesophytes. *Halophytes* are plants of salt marshes; they frequently resemble xerophytes in their structure, for, like xerophytes they endure physiological dryness.

4) MINERAL SALTS. Absence of essential minerals results in growth abnormalities. The absence of nitrogen prevents protein synthesis, absence of iron prevents chlorophyll formation, etc.

5) OXYGEN. Normal growth of most plants occurs only when abundant oxygen is present, since oxygen is important in respiration.

6) OTHER GASES. Excessive carbon dioxide, smoke gas, illuminating gas usually have a stunting or injurious effect on growth. CO_2 is essential in photosynthesis.

7) POISONS. Arsenic, mercury, alcohol, and other poisons injure and kill plants.

8) MANY OTHER FACTORS INFLUENCE GROWTH. Among these are contact, pressure, electricity, wind, parasites, etc.

(RESPONSES)

Irritability, a fundamental property of living protoplasm, is the ability to receive stimuli and to react to them (Fig. 23).

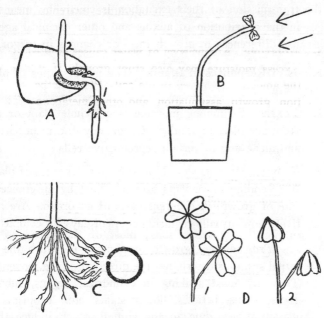

Fig. 23. Some plant responses. A. Geotropism in corn seedling: 1. positive geotropism of root; 2. negative geotropism of shoot. B. Positive phototropism of seedling stem. C. Hydrotropism of roots, growing toward break in drainage pipe. D. Sleep movement of sorrel leaves: 1. day position; 2. night position.

(**Stimuli Which Induce Plant Responses.**) Light, temperature, moisture, contact, gravitational force, gases, chemical agents are the chief stimuli which induce plant responses.

The response of an organ *toward* a stimulus is called a *positive response*. A reaction away from a stimulus is a *negative response*.

Reception of Stimuli. In most cases, reception by plants is diffuse, i.e., stimuli affect many cells. In other cases there are special cells which receive stimuli, especially the stimulus of gravity. Usually there are no special sense organs in plants as there are in animals.

Transmission of Excitation. The irritation induced by a stimulus is termed *excitation*. Often the regions of reception and of reaction are some distance apart. Thus, there must be a transmission of excitation between these regions. Plants lack nerves and the transmission of their excitation is chiefly by means of changes in the distribution of auxins and other chemical agents, which cause differences in growth rates or changes in turgor.

Kinds of Responses in Plants. The major types of plant responses are:

1. TAXIES. Swimming movements of whole plant or part from one place to another. Occur only in certain bacteria and algae and in certain reproductive cells.

2. GROWTH MOVEMENTS. Most common responses of plants. Are bending movements brought about by differences in rate of growth in different parts of an organ. Are relatively slow, usually requiring hours or days for completion.

   Tropisms are growth movements in which the external stimulus determines the direction of the movement. They are most striking in cylindrical organs, such as roots, stems, petioles, flower stalks, etc. Tropisms are classified according to the stimuli which induce them, e.g., *phototropism* (growth toward or away from light), *geotropism* (growth toward or away from earth's gravitational force), *hydrotropism* (growth toward water), *chemotropism,* (growth toward or away from chemicals), etc. *Negative* tropisms are those in which the direction of bending is *away* from the stimulus (e.g., negative geotropism of stems, which turn upward), *positive* tropisms are those in which the direction of bending is *toward* the stimulus (e.g., positive phototropism of stems and leaves). Tropisms are very important, for they usually result in advantageous orientation toward stimuli. *Nastic* movements are growth movements which occur when the stimulus affects all parts of an organ uniformly or when the stimulus calls forth a movement the direction of which is more or less independent of the direction of the stimulus. Nasties are especially characteristic of flattened organs such as young leaves, opening bud scales and flower petals, etc. The principal external stimuli which induce nasties are light and temperature changes; in some nasties the stimuli seem to be internal.

3. TURGOR MOVEMENTs are less common than growth movements, are more rapid, often being completed in a few seconds or minutes. Are caused by changes in turgor pressure in certain cells, not by growth differences. Principal stimuli are changes in light and temperature, and contact. Examples of turgor movements are *sleep movements* (folding of leaves of clover, etc.), movements of Sensitive Plant (*Mimosa*), movements of Venus' fly-trap and sundew, guard cell movements, etc. Some turgor movements are advantageous (Venus' fly-trap, sundew, guard cells), others seem to have little or no value (sleep movements).

Other Features of Plant Responses. The amount of energy expended in a response is usually much greater than the energy involved in the stimulus.

In responses, the *presentation time* is the minimum time during which a stimulus must act in order to bring about just the beginning of a response. The *latent time* is the time which elapses between the end of the presentation time and the beginning of the reaction. The *reaction time* is the period from the beginning of the presentation time until the beginning of the movement.

Chapter XIII

FLOWER STRUCTURE AND ACTIVITIES

The onset of flowering is determined by several factors: heredity, photoperiods, food reserves, and often critical temperatures. These factors appear to cause manufacture of a flowering-hormone, *florigen*, the chemical nature of which is not known. A flower is not a single organ, but is a branch bearing leaf-like and stem-like parts on a short axis.

Flowers, like other types of twigs, develop from buds. Flowers develop from flower-buds (e.g., in morning-glories, roses) or from mixed buds (e.g., in buckeye). Floral organs develop as protuberances from the growing tip of a bud in basipetal order. The tip of a floral twig does not elongate as much as the tip of a vegetative twig, as a result of which the floral organs are crowded at the apex of the twig, not distributed along the twig, as are leaves.

THE PARTS OF A TYPICAL COMPLETE FLOWER

A complete flower bears four kinds of floral organs (Fig. 24). The tip of the floral twig to which these organs are attached is the *receptacle*. The four kinds are:

Sepals. The outermost circle of leaves, usually green in color, sometimes of the same color as the petals. Sepals protect the inner parts of the flower in the bud. The sepals are known collectively as the *calyx*.

Petals. A circle of organs inside the sepals. Are usually brightly colored, and often secrete aromatic substances and *nectar* (concentrated sugar solution). Petals serve to attract insects, which are necessary for pollination of most flowers. The numbers of sepals and of petals are usually the same in the same species. The petals are known collectively as the *corolla*.

Stamens. Floral organs inside the petals. A stamen consists of a slender stalk (*filament*), with a pollen-bearing *anther* at its apex. Stamens produce pollen, which effects fertilization and initiates the development of the ovule, which becomes the seed.

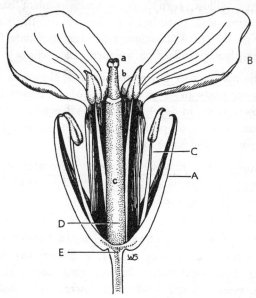

Fig. 24. A complete flower. A. Sepal. B. Petal. C. Stamen (anther and filament). D. Pistil; a. stigma, b. style, c. ovary. E. Receptacle.

Pistil. A structure in the center of the flower, composed of one organ (*simple pistil*) or of several fused organs (*compound pistil*). An ovule-bearing organ is termed a *carpel*. A pistil has a hollow, swollen base (*ovary*), with a slender stalk (*style*) arising from the ovary, and a slight enlargement (*stigma*) at the top of the style. Within the ovary the undeveloped seeds (*ovules*) are produced. The ovules are attached to the inside of the ovary on structures called *placentae*.

The sepals and petals are known as *accessory parts*, since they are not directly concerned with reproduction. The stamens and pistil(s) are the *essential parts* of a flower.

VARIATIONS IN FLOWER STRUCTURE

1. A complete flower (e.g., rose) has four kinds of flower parts. An incomplete flower lacks one or more of these kinds of parts (e.g., elm, wheat).

2. A *perfect* flower has both stamens and pistil (e.g., rose). An *imperfect* flower has stamens or pistil, but not both (e.g., willow, corn). A *monoecious* plant has stamen-bearing and pistil-bearing flowers on the same plant (e.g., corn). A *dioecious* plant has staminate flowers on one plant, *pistillate* on another (e.g., willow).

3. The numbers of flower parts vary. Monocots have their flower parts in 3s or multiples of 3. Dicots have their flower parts in 5s, 4s, or 2s, less frequently in 3s. The basic number of parts is usually the same for all floral organs of the same species.

4. Flower parts may be completely separate, or they may be fused in varying degree. Floral organs of the same kind may be fused together, or to the floral organs of another type.

5. The *symmetry* of flowers varies. In flowers with *radial symmetry* (e.g., rose, tulip), a flower may be divided into two equal halves by any longitudinal cut through the center of the flower. In flowers with *bilateral symmetry* (e.g., snapdragon, sweet pea), longitudinal division into two equal halves can be made by but a single cut through the center of the flower. In a flower with *irregular symmetry* (e.g., canna) there can be no division into two equal halves.

6. *Ovary position* varies in flowers (Fig. 25). In *hypogynous* flowers (e.g., tulip), the sepals, petals, and stamens are attached to the receptacle under the ovary, which is said to be *superior*. In *epigynous* flowers (e.g., honeysuckle), the pistil is sunken into the receptacle, with sepals, petals, and stamens attached above the ovary, which is termed *inferior*. In *perigynous* flowers (e.g., cherry), the pistil is in the bottom of a concave receptacle to the edges of which the sepals, stamens, and petals are

attached; in such a flower, the ovary may be *superior* or *half-inferior*.

7. <u>Arrangement of flower parts varies.</u> The flower organs may be arranged in separate circles or *whorls* (e.g., in lilies), or in a continuous *spiral* (e.g., in magnolias). The former arrangement is termed *cyclic*, the latter *spiral*.

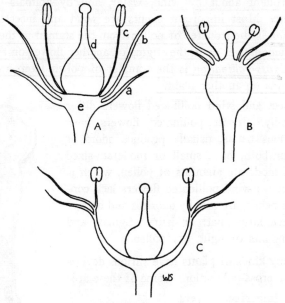

Fig. 25. Ovary position in flowers. A. Superior ovary; a. sepal, b. petal, c. stamen, d. pistil, e. receptacle. B. Inferior ovary. C. Perigynous flower.

8. <u>The sizes, shapes, and colors of flower parts also vary.</u>

9. <u>Flowers also vary in their positions on the plant.</u> Flowers may be borne singly (tulips, magnolias), or in clusters (*inflorescences*), as in snapdragons or sunflowers. In a sunflower, the individual flowers are minute and are borne in large numbers on a flattened disc; the central flowers (*disc-flowers*) of the disc have small radial corollas, the marginal ones (*ray-flowers*) have large yellow bilateral corollas. Such an inflorescence comprising numerous small flowers is called a *head* and is found also in asters, chrysanthemums, etc. Such plants are called *com-*

posites. The stalk of an inflorescence, from which the *pedicels* of individual flowers branch, is termed the *peduncle*. In solitary flowers, the stalk is called the peduncle.

POLLINATION

Pollination is the transfer of pollen from a stamen to a stigma. It is brought about by wind, water, and by animals—insects, birds, etc. Most important agents are wind and insects. *Self-pollination* is the transfer of pollen from the stamen to the stigma of the same flower or to the stigma of another flower on the same plant. *Cross-pollination* is the transfer of pollen from an anther to a stigma on another plant.

Insect and wind pollinated flowers differ structurally. Insect pollinated flowers have conspicuous petals, usually produce odors or nectar or both, have small or moderate-sized stigmas, moderate amounts of pollen, which is often sticky; wind pollinated flowers lack conspicuous petals, are usually odorless and nectarless, have large, flat, or hairy stigmas, and large amounts of light, dry pollen.

Many kinds of plants have various devices to ensure cross-pollination. Some of these are:

1. Imperfect flowers.
2. Difference in time of maturation of stamens and stigma of the same flower.
3. Chemical incompatability between stigma and pollen. Pollen grains will not germinate on stigmas of same plant.
4. Specialized structural devices—spring arrangements (e.g., *Salvia*), peculiarities of style and stamen structure (e.g., primrose, etc.)

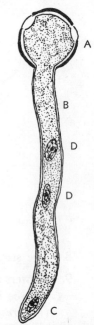

Fig. 26. Pollen grain with tube. A. Pollen grain. B. Pollen tube. C. Tube nucleus. D. Sperm nuclei.

THE DEVELOPMENT OF POLLEN GRAINS AND OVULES

(1) Pollen mother cells are produced in the anther sacs. Each mother cell forms four pollen grains. *Meiosis*, or reduc-

tion division, occurs when pollen grains are formed from
pollen mother cells. Each nucleus in a pollen grain thus
has half the number of chromosomes of the body cells.
Each pollen grain (Fig. 26) is a microscopic one-celled
structure, with two nuclei, a *tube nucleus* and a *generative
nucleus*. Pollen grains are usually yellowish or orange
in color, less frequently white, purple, or some other
color. Pollen grains are shed usually by the splitting
open of an anther.

(2) An ovule (Fig. 27) develops inside the ovary, to the
inside of which it is attached by a *placenta* and by a stalk,
or *funiculus*. The ovules extend into the cavity or cavities

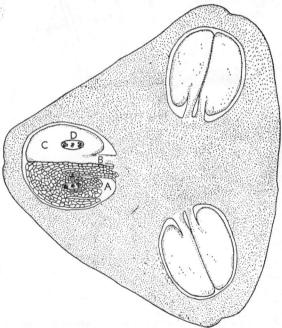

Fig. 27.   Cross-section of lily ovary showing three carpels.   A. Locule.
B. Funiculus.   C. Ovule.   D. Embryo sac.

(*locules*) of the ovary. An ovule ready for fertilization
has several layers (*integuments*) of cells on its surface.
Inside the integuments is the *embryo sac,* which at maturity usually contains eight nuclei, three at one end,
two in the center, and three at the other end. Reduction

division occurs in the *spore mother cell* in the ovule. One of the spores formed from a spore mother cell develops into the embryo sac. At the end of the ovule opposite the funiculus end is a pore (*micropyle*), an opening where the integuments have not closed. One of

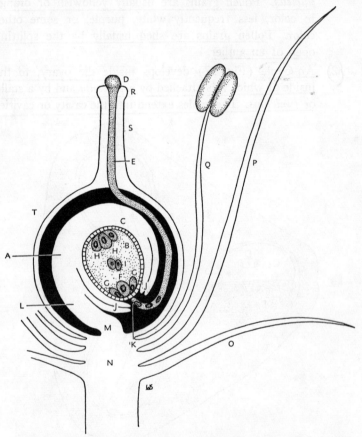

Fig. 28. Longitudinal section of flower, showing pollen-tube growth and ovule structure. A. Ovule. B. Embryo-sac (megagametophyte). C. Nucellus. D. Pollen grain. E. Pollen tube. F. Egg nucleus. G. Synergids. H. Antipodals. I. Polar nuclei. J. Integuments. K. Pollen tube entering micropyle, with one tube and two sperm nuclei. L. Funiculus. M. Placenta. N. Receptacle. O. Sepal. P. Petal. Q. Stamen. R. Stigma. S. Style. T. Ovary.

the nuclei at the micropylar end of the embryo sac is the egg; the other two at this end are the *synergids*. The two nuclei in the center of the embryo sac are the

fusion
polar nuclei. The other three at the other end of the embryo sac are the *antipodals.*

POLLEN TUBE GROWTH AND FERTILIZATION (Fig. 28)

Following the landing of a pollen grain on a stigma, which is often covered by a sticky fluid, hairs, or roughened protuberances which hold the pollen grains, the following incidents occur in order:

(1) The pollen grain swells and germinates, forming a *pollen tube,* which grows down through the style by digesting some of the stylar cells or by growth through a stylar canal, and which enters the ovary. The growth of the pollen tube is controlled by the tube nucleus.

(2) A pollen tube enters the micropyle of an ovule in the ovary and discharges into the embryo sac two *sperm nuclei,* which develop from the division of the generative nucleus.

(3) One sperm fuses with the egg nucleus, thus forming a *zygote,* or fertilized egg.

(4) The other sperm fuses with the two polar nuclei to form the *endosperm nucleus.* This behavior of both sperms is known as *double fertilization.* The endosperm nucleus has three times the chromosome number of an egg or sperm, since it is the result of triple fusion.

(5) The tube nucleus, synergids, and antipodals disintegrate.

(6) The zygote by numerous cell divisions develops into the *embryo* of the seed.

(7) The endosperm nucleus develops by numerous cell divisions into the *endosperm* (food storage) tissue of the seed.

(8) The integuments become the seed coats of the seed.

(9) Following fertilization, the ovary and its ovules increase in size. In some plants, fruits develop without fertilization (e.g., navel orange), a condition known as *parthenocarpy.*

CHAPTER XIV

FRUITS AND SEEDS

A fruit is a matured *ovary*, a seed is a matured *ovule*. Often fruits have adhering to them other floral parts. Such fruits are called *accessory fruits*.

FRUITS (Fig. 29)

The cavities of a fruit, within which the seeds are produced, are called *locules*. The wall of a ripened ovary is termed the *pericarp*. The pericarp consists of three layers of tissue which are not always distinguishable; the outermost wall, or *exocarp*, is usually only one cell thick, the *mesocarp*, or middle wall, is thicker than the exocarp and contains the conducting tissues, and the *endocarp*, or innermost tissue, surrounds the locules.

Fruits are classified as follows:

Simple Fruits. A simple fruit develops from a single ovary of a single flower.

1. FLESHY FRUITS. Are soft and pulpy at maturity.
   a. *Berry*. The entire pericarp becomes soft and fleshy (e.g., grape, tomato, banana, watermelon, orange).
   b. *Drupe*. The exocarp and mesocarp are soft and fleshy, the endocarp becomes hard and stony (*pit*). Inside the pit is usually one seed (sometimes two or three), (e.g., peach, cherry).

2. DRY FRUITS. Are dry and hard or papery at maturity.
   a. *Dehiscent Fruits*. Split open along one or more definite seams (*sutures*). (1) Capsule. A dry fruit formed from a compound ovary (composed of more than one fused carpels), (e.g., poppy, snapdragon). (2) Legume. Develops from a single carpel, splits along

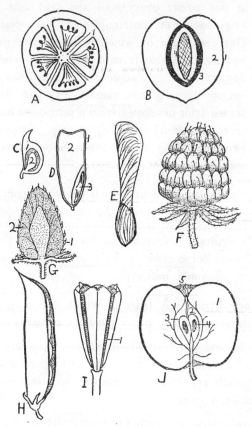

Fig. 29. Some common types of fruits. A. Berry (tomato): 1. pericarp; 2. seeds. B. Drupe (plum): 1. exocarp; 2. mesocarp; 3. stony endocarp; 4. seed. C. Achene (buttercup): 1. fruit; 2. seed. D. Caryopsis (corn): 1. fused fruit and seed coats; 2. endosperm of seed; 3. embryo. E. Samara (maple). F. Aggregate fruit (raspberry). G. Accessory fruit of strawberry: 1. achene; 2. receptacle. H. Legume (lima bean). I. Capsule (tulip): 1. seeds. J. Accessory fruit of apple (pome): 1. cortex of receptacle; 2. pith of receptacle; 3. pericarp; 4. seed; 5. remnants of calyx.

two seams (*sutures*), (e.g., pea, bean). (3) <u>Fol-licle</u>. Develops from a single carpel, splits along one seam (e.g., larkspur, columbine). (4) Silique. Develops from two carpels, which separate at maturity, leaving a partition wall (e.g., mustard).

b. *Indehiscent Fruits*. Do not split by definite seams or pores at maturity.

(1) <u>Achene</u>. One seed attached to inside of ovary

at one point; ovary wall and seed coat separable (e.g., sunflower, buttercup). (2) Caryopsis (grain). One seed, coat of which is fused with ovary wall and not separable from it (e.g., corn, wheat). (3) Samara. One or two seeds. Pericarp has wing-like outgrowths (e.g., ash, maple). (4) Nut. Hard, one-seeded fruit developed from a compound ovary (e.g., acorn, hazelnut). (5) Schizocarp. Carpels usually two, separating at maturity. Each carpel has one seed (e.g., carrot, parsnip).

Aggregate Fruits. A fruit which develops from separate simple ovaries of a single flower (e.g., blackberries, raspberries).

Multiple Fruits. A fruit which develops from the ovaries of several flowers borne close together on a common axis (e.g., Osage orange, pineapple, mulberry).

Accessory Fruits. A fruit in which the major portion consists of tissue other than ovary tissue. Common types are:

1. Apples and pears, in which the true fruits are the walls and locules of the core and the fleshy portion is swollen receptacle and calyx surrounding the core. Such a fruit is called a *pome*.

2. Strawberries, in which the true fruits are tiny achenes on the surface of a much enlarged, sweet, fleshy receptacle.

SEED STRUCTURE (Fig. 30)

A seed consists of a *seed coat*, which develops from the integuments of the ovule, an *embryo*, which develops from a fertilized egg or zygote, and *endosperm*, a food-storage tissue, which develops from the endosperm nucleus of the embryo sac. In most cases, the embryo of a seed begins to digest and utilize the food stored in the endosperm when the seed is planted. In other seeds (beans, peas) the embryo digests and absorbs the endosperm before the seed leaves its parent plant; thus, in such seeds at maturity there is no endosperm present.

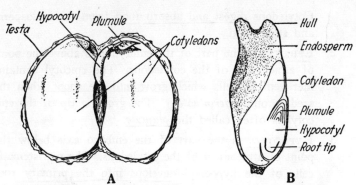

Fig. 30. Seed structure. A. A lima bean laid open to show the parts of the embryo, natural size. B. Longitudinal section of a grain of corn, X 3.*

The structure and functions of these parts are:

Seed Coat. Usually tough and partly impervious to water. Prevents excessive evaporation of water from inner parts of seed, often prevents entry of parasites. Hard seed coats may prevent mechanical injury. Various structures may be visible on the surface of a seed coat:

1. HILUM—a scar left by the breaking of the seed from its stalk.

2. MICROPYLE—a small pore near the hilum.

3. RAPHE—a ridge on the seed, caused by the bending of the seed against the seed stalk.

Endosperm. Cells of the endosperm have 3x chromosome number, since they develop from the endosperm nucleus, which is formed by the fusion of three nuclei—two polar nuclei and a sperm nucleus. The endosperm stores foods—starch, proteins, oils, etc. Some seeds store chiefly starch (wheat), others store chiefly proteins (beans, peas), others chiefly oils (coconut, lily). The seeds of legumes (beans, peas, clover) have no endosperm at maturity, as described above.

Embryo. The embryo, or miniature plant of the seed, consists of:

1. COTYLEDON(s), or seed leaves. Seeds of monocotyledons have one, seeds of dicotyledons have two cotyledons.

---

* Reprinted by permission from *Fundamentals of Biology*, by A. W. Haupt, published by the McGraw-Hill Book Company.

Cotyledons <u>digest and absorb food</u> from the endosperm and <u>store food</u>.

2. Epicotyl is the part of the embryo axis above the point of attachment of the cotyledons. The epicotyl contains meristematic cells which <u>grow into the shoot</u> when the seed sprouts (*germinates*). The growing tip of the epicotyl is often called the *plumule*.

3. Hypocotyl is the part of the embryro axis below the point of attachment of the cotyledons. The meristematic cells of the hypocotyl <u>develops into the primary root</u> when the seed sprouts. The growing tip of the hypocotyl is sometimes called the *radicle*.

Seeds vary in structure in different kinds of plants. Three common types are the following:

1. Bean. A mature bean seed has two large fleshy cotyledons, no endosperm, and a small embryo axis, with a pair of tiny leaves at the apex of the epicotyl.

2. Castor Bean. A mature seed has two flat, thin cotyledons, a short epicotyl and hypocotyl. The embryro is embedded in a large, oily endosperm. A large spongy structure called the *caruncle* lies at one end of the seed.

3. Grain (e.g., corn). A mature "seed" (caryopsis, or one-seeded fruit) has a large horny or mealy endosperm (sometimes both), moderate-sized embryo, consisting of a shield-shaped cotyledon, an epicotyl covered by a sheath (*coleoptile*), and a hypocotyl covered by a sheath (*coleorhiza*). The seed coat and pericarp are fused.

SEED GERMINATION

In seed germination, a seed takes up water and swells, food is digested, respiration increases, assimilation and cell division occur, following which the embryo grows and the seed coat is ruptured. The hypocotyl is usually the first part of the embryo to emerge from the seed coat; this is advantageous, for the young root can immediately begin to absorb the water and minerals necessary for growth. Following the emergence of the hypocotyl is that of the epicotyl. A sprouted embryo is termed a *seedling*.

The pattern of germination varies in different species, as shown by:

1. BEAN. The lower part of the hypocotyl becomes the root. The upper part is crook-shaped and pushes the cotyledons and epicotyl above the soil surface. The crook in the hypocotyl forces an opening through the soil and pulls the cotyledons and epicotyl up through this opening. Cotyledons dry and fall after giving up their food.

2. CASTOR BEAN. Similar to bean in that part of hypocotyl and cotyledons rise above soil. Cotyledons are flat and leaf-like, become green, persist longer than those of bean. Some of the endosperm is carried above ground with the cotyledons.

3. PEAS. Upper part of hypocotyl does not grow above ground; thus, cotyledons remain below soil.

4. GRAIN (CORN). Cotyledon remains in soil. Primary root system soon dies. Adventitious roots develop and form permanent root system.

Seed germination is influenced by various external and internal conditions.

External Conditions.

1. MOISTURE. Seeds must have abundant moisture to germinate. Excessive moisture may cause rotting if oxygen is excluded. Water causes swelling of seed, and is necessary for digestion, translocation, and growth.

2. OXYGEN. Seeds must respire to germinate and must have oxygen for aerobic respiration. Lack of oxygen causes growth of anaerobic bacteria which cause rotting.

3. TEMPERATURE. Most seeds will not germinate if the temperature falls close to freezing or rises above 115° F. Most favorable temperatures are 70-85° F.

4. OTHER EXTERNAL FACTORS which influence seed germination are light, soil acidity, carbon dioxide, etc.

Internal Conditions.

1. Presence of *auxins* (growth regulators).

2. Sufficient stored food.

3. Completion of *dormancy*. Dormancy is a period of relative rest required by most seeds before they can germinate. Dormancy may be due to: undeveloped embryos, thick seed coats which render absorption of oxygen or water difficult or which resist swelling and growth of embryo, necessity of "after-ripening," or gradual chemical changes in embryo. Dormancy is a means of carrying seeds through a period unfavorable to active growth. Since seeds have low water content, they are resistant to many environmental factors which would be injurious to actively growing tissues.

Seed Viability is the ability of seeds to sprout. Most seeds remain viable for not more than five or six years. Some remain viable for only a few weeks (orchids). Others may retain viability for three or four hundred years (Indian lotus). Dry, cool storage conditions favor prolonged viability. Loss of viability seems to be due mainly to coagulation of protoplasm.

SEED AND FRUIT DISPERSAL

Dispersal is the spread of seeds or fruits. Dispersal is brought about by the following:

1. WINGS. Elm, maple fruits; catalpa seeds. Dispersed by wind.

2. PLUMES. Dandelion fruits, milkweed seeds. Dispersed by wind.

3. SPINES AND BARBS. Cocklebur fruits. Dispersed by animals and man, to whose fur or clothing they stick.

4. AIR SPACES OR CORKY FLOATS. Enable fruits and seeds to float in water. Coconut.

5. MINUTE SEEDS. Blown by wind. Orchids.

6. FLESHY FRUITS. Eaten by animals, seeds scattered with feces.

7. NUTS. Buried in ground by squirrels, etc.

8. EXPLOSIVE FRUITS burst and scatter seeds. Touch-me-not, oxalis.

CHAPTER XV

VARIATION AND HEREDITY

One of the striking characteristics of living organisms is their reproduction of similar offspring, which are not merely of the same species as their parents but which often resemble their parents more than other individuals of the same species. However, offspring are never exact duplicates of their parents. The tendency of offspring to be like their parents is _heredity_. The tendency of offspring to differ among themselves and from their parents is called _variation_.

VARIATIONS

Variations within a species are of three common kinds:

(1) _fluctuations_
Environmental Modifications. These are differences brought about by differing environments which may surround individuals of the same species. Individuals of the same plant species growing in different types of soils, under different rainfall and temperature conditions, etc. show differences in size, rate of growth, leaf size, vigor, etc. These environmentally induced modifications are not inherited, except possibly if the differences in the environment continue for thousands of years. Environmental differences affect the body cells, not the sex cells, at least not for many years.

(2) Mutations ("Sports"). Sudden small or large variations of unpredictable nature. They are caused by changes in chromosomes. Mutations are heritable and are usually passed on from generation to generation. Mutations may develop in seeds or in buds; these are called respectively _seed_ and _bud mutations_. Among the important plants which have arisen by mutation are navel oranges, nectarines, and types of Boston ferns.

(3) Combinations. These are variations in the offspring of parents which possess heritable differences. These parental differences combine in various ways in the offspring and are heritable. An offspring of parents with heritable differences is termed a *hybrid*. Combinations differ from mutations in that they develop only as a result of the breeding of two parents with heritable differences, whereas mutations arise spontaneously from a single parent or from parents essentially alike.

HEREDITY

History of Study. Fundamental laws of heredity were discovered by Gregor Mendel, an Austrian monk, who in 1866 published the results of his work on inheritance in garden peas. Since Mendel, many other biologists have studied inheritance; the large amount of information on this subject constitutes the science of *genetics*. At first it was thought that all hereditary phenomena followed the laws discovered by Mendel, but more recently many exceptions to these laws have been found.

Mendel's Experiments and Conclusions.

1. SINGLE-CHARACTER (MONOHYBRID) CROSSES. Mendel crossed a tall pea plant with a dwarf type of pea plant. He placed pollen from flowers of the tall pea on the stigmas of dwarf pea flowers, and vice versa. When the seeds resulting from this cross were planted, the generation which they produced (F_1 generation) consisted entirely of tall plants. When the flowers of these F_1 tall plants were self-pollinated, they produced seeds which were planted and grew into the next generation (F_2), which consisted of both tall and dwarf plants in the ratio of three tall to one dwarf. Of these tall plants, two out of three were like the F_1 tall plants; that is, when self-pollinated, they produced both tall and dwarf plants in the ratio of 3:1. The remaining third of the tall F_2 plants produced only tall plants. The dwarf F_2 plants produced only dwarf plants. Thus half of the F_2 plants were *hybrids,* like the F_1, one quarter of the F_2 plants were like the tall grandparent (*pure dominant*)

and one quarter were like the dwarf grandparent (*pure recessive*). A *dominant* characteristic is one which masks an opposite characteristic when both occur together, a *recessive* character is one which is masked or hidden by a dominant. In this experiment, tallness is dominant, dwarfness is recessive.

Mendel crossed other types of peas differing in other characters and found the same results and F_2 ratios. He found yellow color dominant over green, smooth seed coats dominant over wrinkled, etc.

A *monohybrid cross* is one between parents differing in a single character.

  2. TWO-CHARACTER (DIHYBRID) CROSS. Mendel crossed a pea variety with yellow, round seeds and a pea variety with green, wrinkled seeds. All of F_1 plants produced only yellow, round seeds (yellowness was dominant over greenness, roundness over wrinkledness). Mendel grew these F_1 seeds to flowering, then allowed them to be self-pollinated. The F_2 generation which they produced bore four kinds of seeds: some like one grandparent (yellow, round), some like the other grandparent (green, wrinkled), and two *new combinations*: green round and yellow wrinkled. These four kinds of seeds in the F_2 appeared in approximately this ratio: nine yellow round, three green round, three yellow wrinkled, and one green wrinkled. Because of dominance, the appearance of these four types does not correspond in all cases with the hereditary constitution of these plants; though there are four kinds of plants from the standpoint of appearance, there are nine kinds from the standpoint of hereditary (genetic) constitution.

A *dihybrid cross* is one between parents differing in two characters.

  3. MENDEL'S LAWS. From Mendel's work on mono- and dihybrid crosses, four laws may be stated:

  a. *The Law of Dominance*—described above.

b. *The Law of Segregation*—hereditary determiners may come together in one generation (F_1) and may then separate when that generation reproduces and forms offspring (F_2).

c. *The Law of Unit Characters*—each hereditary determiner is an independent unit in a cell and behaves independently of other determiners.

d. *The Law of Independent Assortment*—the hereditary determiners which come together in one generation may separate and combine in various ways in the next generation (e.g., the F_2 of a di-hybrid cross).

Since Mendel's work, it has been shown that there are exceptions to these laws. Not all hereditary determiners behave as independent units, dominance is absent in many pairs of determiners, etc.

✱ Physical Basis of Heredity (Fig. 31).

1. Chromosomes are the largest identifiable rod-like masses of chromatin in the nucleus at mitosis. Chromatin is organized into units, several of which are borne in linear fashion on a chromosome. Each of these units (*hereditary determiners,* or *genes*) influences a single trait of an organism. Every chromosome bears numerous genes.

2. The hereditary connection between one generation and another is by means of the chromosomes of the sex cells (eggs and sperms) which fuse in pairs at fertilization.

3. All of the *body cells* of plants and animals have two sets of paired chromosomes; one set is a descendant of the chromosomes which came from the parental sperm and is made up of chromosomes like those of the sperm, the other set is a descendant of chromosomes which came from the parental egg. These chromosomes are paired; that is, for every chromosome of the male set, there is a chromosome of the female set bearing similar genes in similar order. In organisms with odd chromosome numbers in their body cells, all of the chromosomes except one are usually paired. Thus, every body cell contains

a number of paired (*homologous*) chromosomes; this number is called the *diploid number*. This number is usually constant for every body cell of the species (e.g., 16 chromosomes in onions; 8 of these are maternal in origin, 8 paternal).

4. When a plant or animal prepares to form sex cells (eggs or sperms) a type of nuclear division called *meiosis* occurs. This process consists of two divisions: a first division in which the paired chromosomes *separate* (segregation) but *do not split,* as a result of which the two cells produced from the parent cell have *half* the number of chromosomes of the parent cell. This is termed the *haploid* chromosome number. Following this first division, there occurs a second division, in which the chromosomes split longitudinally and the halves of each chromosome move in opposite directions. Thus, as a result of the meiotic divisions, four cells with the haploid chromosome number arise from the original parent cell. In most plants, meiosis does not occur at the time of formation of the sex cells, but occurs some time before their formation—namely, in spore-formation at the beginning of the gametophyte generation (see Alternation of Generations, Chapter XVI, p. 113). When an egg and a sperm fuse, their haploid chromosome sets added together produce the diploid number which persists through all body cells of the offspring until it reaches sexual maturity, whereupon it produces haploid sex cells by meiosis.

5. The paired genes or paired chromosomes are alike in an individual which is a pure-breeding individual (e.g., the tall and the dwarf parent peas used in Mendel's monohybrid experiment). Thus, when meiosis occurs and the paired chromosomes or genes separate, each cell formed has chromosomes and genes like the other sex cells of that individual. The fusion of sex cells with the same paired genes produces an offspring like the parent. In a hybrid individual (e.g., in the F_1 generation) which is a product of a cross between different kinds of parents, however, the chromosomes which separate at meiosis do

not all bear similar genes, for they have come from two different types of parents. Thus, the sex cells produced by such a hybrid are of different kinds with respect to their genes; they are not all alike, as in pure-breeding organisms. As a result of the varying unions of these different kinds of gametes of a hybrid, the offspring of hybrids are of varying types, as seen in the F_2 generation.

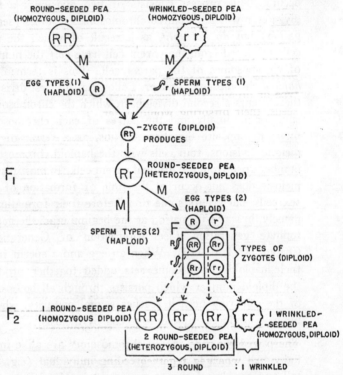

Fig. 31. The mechanics of a monohybrid cross in a case of complete dominance. R represents a dominant gene for round-seededness. r represents a recessive gene for wrinkled-seededness. M represents meiosis (reduction division). F represents fertilization. F_1 represents the first generation from the cross. F_2 represents the second generation from the cross. The behavior of the genes is explained on pages 103-104.

Other Important Features of Heredity.

(1) INCOMPLETE DOMINANCE. When a pure-breeding red four-o'clock plant is crossed with a pure-breeding white four-o'clock, the F_1 generation are all pink-flowered. This

condition is termed *incomplete dominance*, for neither color is able to hide the other; both are expressed in an intermediate color. When the F_1 four-o'clock generation is self-pollinated, the F_2 generation consists of red, pink, and white-flowered plants in the ratio of 1:2:1.

(2) Only varieties of the same species or closely related species can ordinarily be crossed.

(3) The offspring of a hybrid do not "come true." That is, some of them are like their parents. Others may be like more remote ancestors. For this reason, certain cultivated fruits and flowers are propagated by cuttings or grafting, for vegetative propagation never changes the type or organism; if these plants were propagated from seeds, their offspring would differ.

(4) LINKAGE is the inheritance of two or more characters in association with each other, due to the fact that their respective genes are located on the same chromosome. This is an exception to Mendel's Law of Independent Assortment. Mendel failed to discover linkage because the genes for the characters which he studied in peas were borne on separate chromosomes and thus behaved independently. All genes on the same chromosome are ordinarily inherited together; i.e., they show linkage.

(5) CROSSING-OVER. Frequently, linked genes may become separated from each other and may be inherited separately. For example, in peas, smoothness in seeds is linked with the gene for presence of tendrils and normally these are inherited together. Sometimes, however, they separate. This separation of linked genes is explained by an interchange of chromatin between chromosomes, a phenomenon known as *crossing-over*.

The Terminology of Heredity. Important terms used in genetics, other than those already defined are:

1. HOMOZYGOUS—refers to a pure-breeding organism (one with similar paired genes), (e.g., tall and dwarf parents of Mendel's experiment).

2. HETEROZYGOUS—refers to an organism which does not breed true (a hybrid; an organism with differing paired genes), (e.g., the F_1 generation in Mendel's monohybrid experiment).

3. PHENOTYPE—the external appearance of an organism.

4. GENOTYPE—the genetic constitution of an organism.

PLANT BREEDING

Plant breeding is a practical application of the science of genetics. New kinds of plants, often of desirable types, may arise spontaneously by mutation. Also, new kinds of plants may be deliberately developed by *selection* and by *hybridization.*

Selection is based upon the fact that individuals of a given species vary and that some of these variations tend to be inherited. In selection, the individuals with the desired traits are selected from the group in which they are growing. The seeds which the selected individuals produce are planted, and from the plants which these seeds produce, the best individuals are again selected, their seeds saved and planted, etc. By such selection through a number of generations, improved types of plants can be developed. In some plants, these improved types persist; in others, the superior traits gradually disappear and the plants revert to the original types from which they were selected. In the latter case, selection must be practiced repeatedly.

Hybridization involves the crossing of closely related plants, usually in order to bring together in a hybrid desirable traits possessed separately by the parent plants. New combinations of characters are readily produced by such crossing. Hybrids with a desirable combination of characters can usually be propagated indefinitely by vegetative means. If they are propagated by seeds, the characters segregate in the offspring; in other words, the offspring are not all like the hybrid parent.

Chapter XVI

THE CLASSIFICATION OF PLANTS; REPRODUCTION AND ALTERNATION OF GENERATIONS

THE CLASSIFICATION OF PLANTS

The objects of plant classification are to arrange plants in groups for identification and to indicate, wherever possible, relationships among plants. The exact total number of the kinds (*species*) of plants on the earth is not known; about 350,000 species are known at present. The science of classification is *taxonomy*.

The Basis of Classification. In Ancient Greece and in the Middle Ages, plants were classified chiefly on vegetative characters, such as growth habits, leaf structure, etc.

At present, reproductive structures and behavior are chief basis of classification, vegetative characters are of secondary importance. Emphasis is placed on reproductive features because these are less susceptible to the influence of environmental factors than are vegetative parts of plants and are consequently more stable.

Systems of Classification. A *system* of classification is a complete arrangement of the major groups of plants or of all plants into a unified scheme. Different botanists have proposed different systems of classification, because accurate knowledge of true relationships among certain plants is lacking and consequently opinions as to such relationships vary.

A *natural* system attempts to classify organisms on the basis of their true relationships. A natural system is the goal of taxonomy. As more facts about relationship are discovered, artificial systems are replaced by natural systems.

Phylum
Class
Order
Family
Genus
Species

Classificational Units.

1. THE SPECIES is the basic unit in the classification of organisms. A species is a *kind* of living organism—e.g., a dog, a white oak, a sugar maple, etc. A species may be defined technically as the *usually* smallest unit in the classificational system; it is a group of individuals of the same ancestry, of similar structure and behavior, and of stability in nature; that is, the members of a species retain their characteristic features through many generations under natural conditions. In many groups of plants, species are sharply delimited, in other groups, there are no sharp lines between species because of intermediate forms. Sometimes there are different types (*varieties*) of organisms within a species; for example, the various kinds of dogs are all varieties of the dog species; such varieties do not maintain themselves in nature, but are maintained artificially by man.

2. A GENUS (pl. *genera*) is a collection of closely related species. For example, the oak genus is made up of a number of species—red oak, white oak, pin oak, etc. All have certain common major characteristics, but differ in minor ways.

3. A FAMILY is a group of closely related genera. For example, the oak family is made up of the oak genus (*Quercus*), the chestnut genus (*Castanea*), etc. The names of families end usually in "ceae," less frequently "ae"; e.g., the oak family is the *Fagaceae*. These genera have certain traits in common which show them to be related but there are also marked differences among them.

4. AN ORDER is a group of closely related families which have certain common traits but which differ in certain respects. The names of orders end in "ales." The oak order is the *Fagales*.

5. (A CLASS) is a group of related orders. The names of classes end in "ae."

6. (A PHYLUM) is a group of related classes. The names of phyla end in "phyta."

Classification of the Major Plant Groups. A classification which has been popular for many years and which is still used by some botanists is the following:

DIVISION I—*Thallophyta* (simple plants, lacking roots, stems, and leaves and usually having one-celled sex organs):

Subdivision 1—*Algae* (simple plants containing chlorophyll; include pond-scums, algae of tree bark, seaweeds, etc.)

Subdivision 2—*Fungi* (simple plants lacking chlorophyll; include bacteria, yeasts, molds, mushrooms, puffballs, etc.)

DIVISION II—*Bryophyta* (simple plants lacking roots, stems, and leaves and having many-celled sex organs):

Class 1—*Hepaticae* (liverworts)
Class 2—*Musci* (mosses) *leaf, stem, rhizoids*

DIVISION III—*Pteridophyta* (complex plants with vascular tissues, true roots, stems, and leaves, but lacking seeds):

Class 1—*Filicineae* (ferns)
Class 2—*Equisetineae* (horsetails)
Class 3—*Lycopodineae* (club-mosses)

DIVISION IV—*Spermatophyta* (complex plants with vascular tissues, seeds, true roots, stems, and leaves):

Subdivision 1—*Gymnospermae* (cone-bearing plants, such as pines, spruces, and firs)

Subdivision 2—*Angiospermae* (true flowering plants, such as lilies, grasses, geraniums, tulips, and orchids)

Class 1—*Monocotyledonae* (flowering plants with one cotyledon in embryo and flower parts usually in 3's; e.g., lilies, tulips, irises, orchids).

Class 2—*Dicotyledonae* (flowering plants with two cotyledons in embryo and flower parts usually in 5's or 4's; e.g., apples, roses, geraniums, beans).

The system above is artificial in that it does not express the true relationships of all groups; for example, it includes as algae a number of groups of simple plants which are only distantly related, and it does not indicate the close relationship between ferns and seed plants. The following system of classification has become popular because it is more nearly a natural system.

SUBKINGDOM *Thallophyta* (plants not forming embryos)

> Phylum 1—*Cyanophyta* (blue-green algae)
> Phylum 2—*Euglenophyta* (euglenoids)
> Phylum 3—*Chlorophyta* (green algae)
> Phylum 4—*Chrysophyta* (yellow-green algae, golden brown algae, diatoms)
> Phylum 5—*Pyrrophyta* (cryptomonads, dinoflagellates)
> Phylum 6—*Phaeophyta* (brown algae)
> Phylum 7—*Rhodophyta* (red algae)
> Phylum 8—*Schizomycophyta* (bacteria)
> Phylum 9—*Myxomycophyta* (slime molds)
> Phylum 10—*Eumycophyta* (true fungi)

SUBKINGDOM *Embryophyta* (plants forming embryos)

> Phylum 11—*Bryophyta* or *Atracheata* (plants lacking vascular tissues)

>> Class *Musci*—mosses
>> Class *Hepaticae*—liverworts
>> Class *Anthoceratae*—hornworts

> Phylum 12—*Tracheophyta* or *Tracheata* (plants with vascular tissues)

>> Subphylum *Psilopsida*—psilopsids
>> Subphylum *Lycopsida*—club-mosses
>> Subphylum *Sphenopsida*—horsetails and relatives
>> Subphylum *Pteropsida*—ferns and seed plants

>>> Class *Filicineae*—ferns
>>> Class *Gymnospermae*—cone-bearing plants and relatives
>>> Class *Angiospermae*—true flowering plants

>>>> Subclass *Dicotyledonae*
>>>> Subclass *Monocotyledonae*

In this book the second classification above will be followed. Phyla 1 to 7 are called "algae" for convenience, but this is not the official name of a group, as in the older system. Similarly, phyla 8, 9, and 10 are sometimes called "fungi." Unlike fungi, the algae contain chlorophyll and manufacture their own food in photosynthesis.

Scientific Names. Scientific names are derived mainly from Greek and Latin words and are in large degree regulated by agreements passed by botanists at International Botanical Congresses. The advantage of using Latin and Greek is that the elements of these languages are known by most scientists and they constitute an international language of science. Scientific names are often descriptive of traits or places, commemorate people, are based on classical mythology, etc.

Each species of plant or animal has a scientific name composed of two words; the first, which is capitalized, is the name of the genus, the second, not capitalized, is the name of the species. This system of naming organisms is called the "binomial system." It was invented in the seventeenth century and was first used consistently on a large scale by the Swedish taxonomist, Linnaeus (1707-1778). Following each scientific name is an initial or abbreviation which indicates the man who named that species. Examples of scientific names are *Zea Mays L.* (corn), *Rhus cotinoides Nutt* (smoke tree).

REPRODUCTION

The functions of reproduction are the maintenance of the species and the increase in the number of individuals.

There are two main types of reproductive processes:

Sexual Reproduction, which involves the fusion of sex cells (*gametes*) in pairs (*fertilization*). The cell formed by the union of two gametes is called a *zygote*. Meiosis occurs at or before the production of gametes, or sometimes upon the germination of the zygote as in many Thallophytes. Gametes thus have the haploid chromosome number. When two gametes fuse, the zygote has the diploid number, which persists until the individual is mature enough to begin preparation for gamete-production. There are two principal kinds of sexual reproduction:

(1) ISOGAMY, or reproduction by means of gametes which are alike in size and structure (though they may differ physiologically). This is a primitive process found only in certain lower kinds of plants.

(2) HETEROGAMY, the more common and more advanced type of sexual reproduction involves the fusion of two kinds of gametes which are different in size, structure, and physiology. The larger gamete is the *egg*, the smaller the *sperm*.

Asexual (Vegetative) Reproduction, which does not involve the fusion of gametes. A part of a plant separates from a parent plant and grows into another individual. There are several methods of asexual reproduction:

(1) SPORES are specialized, usually one-celled structures which are formed by many plants and which are able to grow into new plants without fusion. Some spores have protoplasmic tails (*cilia* and *flagella*) by means of which they can swim in water. Such spores are termed *zoospores*.

(2) BUDDING is a process in which a one-celled plant forms a small surface protuberance which increases in size until it is almost as large as the parent cell; a wall is formed between the "bud" and the parent cell and the "bud" separates from the parent as a new individual. Budding is not as common as spore-formation. It occurs in yeasts and in the development of the spores of certain higher fungi.

(3) FISSION is the chief method of reproduction in many one-celled plants. It is the division of a one-celled plant into two new one-celled plants.

(4) FRAGMENTATION is the breaking-away of a few or many-celled part of a plant; this fragment is able to grow into a new individual.

(5) BULBS, CORMS, STOLONS, RHIZOMES, TUBERS are asexual reproductive structures of many plants. Plants are propagated asexually by means of cuttings, grafts, etc.

✳ (ALTERNATION OF GENERATIONS)

In most plants, except certain Thallophyta, the life-cycle of an individual is made up of two phases or generations, one of which, the *gametophyte generation,* reproduces sexually, the other of which, the *sporophyte generation,* reproduces asexually by spores. The gametophyte generation produces sex-cells (gametes) which fuse in pairs; the cell formed by such a fusion is the *zygote.* All cells of the gametophyte generation have the single (*haploid*) chromosome number; the fusion of gametes results in the double (*diploid*) chromosome number in the zygote. The zygote grows into the sporophyte generation, all of the cells of which have the diploid chromosome number. The sporophyte generation forms spores, which are haploid and which thus mark the beginning of the gametophyte generation.

✳ Spores are formed from cells of the sporophyte generation called *sporocytes* or *spore mother cells,* which are produced in *sporangia,* or spore cases. Spore mother cells have the diploid chromosome number. The first division of a spore mother cell nucleus is a *meiotic* or *reduction* division (Fig. 32). As explained in Chapter XV, meiosis involves the separation, *not* the splitting, of the paired (homologous) chromosomes of a nucleus and thus produces daughter cells with half the chromosome number of the

Fig. 32. Meiosis (reduction division) in a spore mother cell. A. Spore mother cell, showing diploid set of paired chromosomes. B. Two haploid nuclei resulting from first division of spore mother cell nucleus. C. Four haploid nuclei resulting from division of two haploid nuclei (B). Walls are formed, producing four haploid spores.

mother cell. The two haploid nuclei formed by meiosis in a spore mother cell then divide, usually within a short time, mitotically, forming four haploid nuclei within the spore mother cell wall. Cell walls are formed about these four nuclei, separating them and thus producing four haploid spores which constitute the beginning of the gametophyte generation. The term *maturation* is applied to this series of processes involved in the development of spores from a spore mother cell.

Alternation of generations occurs in some Thallophyta, and in all Bryophyta and Tracheophyta.

In studying the plant groups, students should organize their knowledge about each group according to this outline:

1. STRUCTURE. General body structure.

2. REPRODUCTION. Types and nature of reproduction; alternation of generations.

3. HABITATS AND DISTRIBUTION. Environments commonly inhabited; occurrence in different parts of world.

4. IMPORTANCE TO MAN. Importance in agriculture, industry, etc.

5. EVOLUTIONARY IMPORTANCE. Relationships with other groups; relative position in plant kingdom.

6. COMMON REPRESENTATIVES. Names of typical members of the group.

CHAPTER XVII

THALLOPHYTA: ALGAE

THALLOPHYTA AS A WHOLE

Thallophyta as a whole have these characteristics:

(1.) They lack true roots, stems, and leaves.

(2) Sex cells are produced in rather simple sex organs.

(3) There is a relatively slight degree of tissue differentiation. No xylem, phloem, cambium, pericycle, etc., in most kinds.

(4) They are chiefly water plants, and the land plants are mainly parasites or saprophytes.

(5.) They do not form embryos.

THE ALGAE

Algae consist of seven phyla, six of which will be described in this section. These six phyla include about 20,000 known species, all of which contain chlorophyll and therefore are able to manufacture their own food in photosynthesis. Although they contain chlorophyll, many plants in these phyla are brown, red, or of some other hue as a result of the presence of pigments which mask the green color of chlorophyll.

1. **Phylum Cyanophyta** (blue-green algae) (Fig. 33).

1) STRUCTURE. Contain chlorophyll and a blue pigment (*phycocyanin*), both dissolved in the cytoplasm. A few species are red. No plastids. No organized nuclei, but chromatin granules scattered through cytoplasm. One-celled. Cells often held together in colonies by a mucilagi-

115

nous secretion. Colonies chiefly thread-like (*filamentous*), or clusters or sheets of cells.

2) REPRODUCTION. Entirely asexual, chiefly by fission. A few species form resting "spores."

3.) HABITATS AND DISTRIBUTION. Both in salt and fresh water, chiefly latter. On wet rocks, damp soil, etc. Some in vicinity of hot springs. Widely distributed.

4.) IMPORTANCE TO MAN. Contaminate water supplies, furnish fish food, add organic matter to soil and increase soil fertility. Some poisonous to fish and domesticated animals.

5) COMMON REPRESENTATIVES. *Oscillatoria, Nostoc.*

2. **Phylum Euglenophyta (euglenoids).**

1) STRUCTURE. Are one-celled plants which swim by means of flagella. Are spherical, ovoid, pear-shaped, etc. Each cell contains a nucleus and usually one or more chloroplasts. Green, brownish, reddish, or yellowish green in color. A red *eyespot,* a light perceiving structure, is usually present. In many species, a primitive *gullet* is present, by means of which solid food may be ingested. Cells often remain together in colonies. Possess a mixture of plant and animal characteristics; non-green flagellates are often classified as animals.

2) REPRODUCTION. By cell division or simple gametes.

3.) HABITATS AND DISTRIBUTION. Are water plants, growing in oceans, lakes, ponds, etc. Widely distributed on earth's surface.

4.) IMPORTANCE TO MAN. Food for fish and other water animals; pollute water supplies because of bad odors and taste which they give to water.

5) EVOLUTIONARY IMPORTANCE. Many biologists believe that flagellates are similar to first living organisms on the earth, that possibly both plants and animals have evolved from flagellate-ancestors.

6) COMMON REPRESENTATIVE. *Euglena.*

3. Phylum Chlorophyta (green algae).

1) STRUCTURE. Green in color. Chloroplasts and nuclei present. Some one-celled, some colonial, some multicellular. Most species are filamentous; some form sheets or clusters of cells, others are strictly unicellular. Some species have special *holdfasts,* which anchor the filaments on stones, etc.

2) REPRODUCTION. Both asexual (zoospores, fission, fragmentation) and sexual (isogamy and heterogamy) methods occur.

3.) HABITATS AND DISTRIBUTION. Grow in both salt and fresh water, on wet soil, fence posts, moist stones, tree bark, etc. Chiefly fresh-water. Widely distributed.

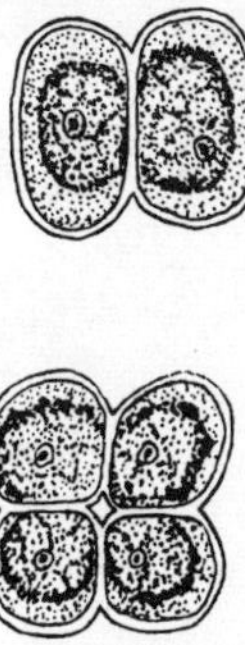

4) IMPORTANCE TO MAN. Pollute water, add oxygen to water and thus benefit fish, furnish food for fish, furnish human food, form carbonates and thus build rock deposits.

5.) COMMON REPRESENTATIVES. Some of the variations in structure and reproduction are shown by the following genera: (1) *Protococcus.* One-celled, found commonly on tree bark. Reproduction by cell-division only (Fig. 34). (2) *Ulothrix.* Filamentous, with holdfasts at bases of filaments. Grows in running water. Reproduces asexually by means of 4-ciliate zoospores, which are formed in 2s, 4s, 8s, or 16s per cell; each zoospore swims, attaches itself to a solid object in water, then grows into a filament. Reproduces also sexually by formation of 32 or 64 2-ciliate isogametes, which are similar to zoospores structurally, though smaller; gametes fuse in pairs and form zygotes. Each zygote, after a resting period, germinates, forms four zoospores, which swim, then attach themselves to solid objects and form filaments (Fig. 35). (3) *Spirogyra.* Filaments growing in fresh water without holdfasts. One or more spiral chloroplasts per cell. Reproduces

Fig. 34.
Protococcus

asexually by fragmentation; does not form asexual spores. Reproduces sexually by isogamy, as follows: two filaments, lying side by side, form protuberances from opposite cells; these protuberances push the threads apart, meet in pairs, fuse at tips into tubes; protoplasm (single gamete) of one cell moves through tube into opposite cell, fuses with protoplasm (gamete) of latter to form a

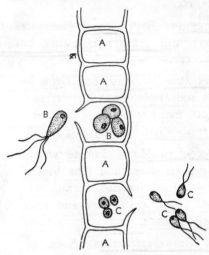

Fig. 35. *Ulothrix.* A. Cells of filament.
B. Zoospores. C. Isogametes.

thick-walled zygote, which after a resting period, undergoes meiosis and grows into a new filament, which is haploid. Sometimes protoplasm of one cell fuses with that of an adjoining cell of same filament (Fig. 36).

(4) *Oedogonium.* Filamentous, attached to solid objects in fresh water. Considerable differentiation among cells. Reproduces asexually by many-ciliate zoospores, which swim about, then attach themselves and grow into new filaments. Reproduces sexually by heterogamy; certain cells of filaments become *oogonia,* each of which contains a single egg; other cells become *antheridia,* each with two ciliated sperms; a sperm swims through a pore in the oogonium, fertilizes the egg in the oogonium. The thick-

walled zygote rests for a time, then forms four zoospores,
each of which, after liberation, grows into a new filament.
The filaments and gametes are haploid, the zygote is

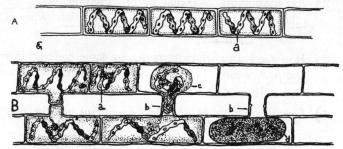

Fig. 36. *Spirogyra.* A. Vegetative filament; a. spiral chloroplasts. B. Conjugating filaments; b. conjugation tubes, c. gamete moving through conjugation tube, d. zygote.

diploid; meiosis occurs in the formation of zoospores
which are haploid. In some species antheridia and oogonia
develop in the same filament, in others, they are formed
on separate filaments (Fig. 37).

6) EVOLUTIONARY IMPORTANCE OF GREEN ALGAE. Some
reproduce only by fission, others by zoospores, isogamy,
heterogamy, etc. Gametes seem to have developed from
zoospores, which they often resemble very closely in structure, though smaller in size (e.g., in *Ulothrix*); in *Oedogonium*, sperms are like zoospores structurally but smaller,
eggs also resemble zoospores. Most primitive type of
sexual reproduction involves union of isogametes like
zoospores (*Ulothrix*); more advanced type involves
union of heterogametes, which differ markedly in size
(*Oedogonium*). In some algae, very slight size difference
among gametes; transitional from isogamy to heterogamy.

4. **Phylum Chrysophyta (yellow-green, golden-brown algae, diatoms).**

1) STRUCTURE. Mostly unicellular and colonial; few multicellular. Cell walls usually composed of two overlapping
halves and impregnated with silica, thus having a harsh
texture. Flagella present or absent. Color of chlorophyll

partly or wholly masked by yellowish or brownish pigments. Nuclei and plastids present.

2.) REPRODUCTION. Asexual by cell division, zoospores, or other types of spores. Sexual reproduction, when it occurs, is isogamous.

3.) HABITATS AND DISTRIBUTION. In damp soil and in fresh and salt water. Occur in enormous numbers in water, especially ocean water.

4.) IMPORTANCE TO MAN. Most important are the diatoms,

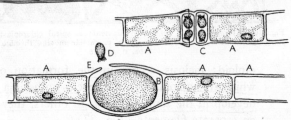

Fig. 37. *Oedogonium*. A. Cells of filament. B. Oogonium with egg. C. Antheridium with sperms. D. Sperm. E. Fertilization pore.

which have beautifully sculptured walls. Diatoms are used in filters in industry, polishes for metals, insulation for pipes and furnaces, dynamite, insulation in refrigerators, and sometimes in tooth-pastes. Much petroleum is of diatom origin. Diatomaceous earth is a rock-like deposit of dead diatom shells and is mined in several parts of the world to obtain material for the uses mentioned above. Diatoms constitute an important food source for fish and other aquatic animals.

5.) COMMON REPRESENTATIVES. Most familiar are the diatoms.

6.) EVOLUTIONARY IMPORTANCE. Exact relationships not known. Some botanists believe them to be related to flagellated, unicellular green algae.

5. Phylum Phaeophyta (brown algae).

1.) STRUCTURE. Largest of algae, most complex structurally, with considerable differentiation (some have sieve tubes), often reaching lengths of several hundred feet. Have large holdfasts. Brownish pigment (*fucoxanthin*) present in addition to chlorophyll. Some filamentous. Many have stem-like, root-like, and leaf-like parts, often with air bladders which give buoyancy.

2.) REPRODUCTION. Some reproduce asexually by zoospores. Sexual reproduction in some by isogamy, some by heterogamy. Alternation of generations in some species (see below).

3.) HABITATS AND DISTRIBUTION. Chiefly in cooler ocean waters, a few in fresh water. Grow attached to rocks, etc., mainly in shallow water.

4.) IMPORTANCE TO MAN. Food for fish and other water animals, source of iodine, mineral salts used as fertilizers and in soap manufacture, food for man and cattle, used in medicinal preparations.

5.) COMMON REPRESENTATIVES.

a. *Ectocarpus:* Filamentous, attached. Forms two types of zoospores—*diploid* and *haploid*. Former grow into diploid plants like their parents, forming more zoospores; latter grow into haploid plants which form isogametes and thus reproduce sexually. This is a primitive type of alternation of generations. Zygotes formed by haploid plants develop into diploid plants which form zoospores. Zoospores and gametes similar structurally. In some species, gametes alike in size, in others size differences occur. Thus, there are some heterogamous species.

b. *Fucus* (Bladder wrack). On rocks in intertidal zones of temperate seas. No asexual reproduction. Mature plant is dichotomously branched thallus, with enlarged branch tips often with air-bladders. Thalli have holdfasts, stem-like parts. In enlarged tips there are small sunken cavities (*conceptacles*), tips of which appear as tiny blisters on branch-tips. Sexual reproduction heterogamous. Conceptacles contain antheridia and oogonia; in some species, these are on separate plants, in others, are produced in same conceptacle. Antheridia produce up to 64 sperms, oogonia usually 8 eggs each. Sperms and eggs escape at maturity through pores at tips of conceptacles into sea water. A sperm fuses with an egg in water to form zygote, which grows into a new plant. Plants are diploid; meiosis occurs at gamete-formation, as in animals but a rare occurrence in higher plants.

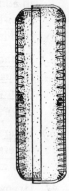

Fig. 38.   Diatom

   c. *Kelps.* Are large, massive brown algae, chiefly on Pacific Coast of U. S. Have holdfasts, often large air-bladders.

6. **Phylum Rhodophyta (red algae).**

   1) STRUCTURE. Chiefly feathery, branched-filamentous, sometimes ribbon-like with gelatinous surfaces. Smaller than most brown algae, rarely more than three or four feet long. Red in color, due to *phycoerythrin,* a red pigment present with chlorophyll.

   2) REPRODUCTION. Asexually by non-motile spores, sexually by non-motile heterogametes. Male gametes are spherical, non-motile, produced in antheridia. Male gametes carried by water to female sex organs (*carpogonia*). Each carpogonium has an elongated tip (*trichogyne*), to which a sperm may adhere. Wall of trichogyne near sperm dissolves, nucleus of sperm passes down trichogyne and fuses with female gamete nucleus at base of trichogyne. Zygote produces numerous short branches, on which are borne *carpospores.* In some red algae, carpospores grow into new plants which bear carpogonia and antheridia. In others, carpospores grow into plants which look like plants that produce carpogonia and antheridia, but which form not gametes, but asexual spores in clusters of four (*tetraspores*). Tetraspores grow into plants which produce carpogonia and antheridia, with female and male gametes respectively. Life cycle in such red algae con-

sists of two alternating phases: haploid, gamete-bearing plants, and diploid, tetrasporic plants; meiosis occurs at tetraspore formation, so that tetraspores are haploid.(η)? Thus, alternation of generations in some red algae.

3) HABITATS AND DISTRIBUTION. Chiefly warmer waters of oceans. Few fresh water. Often at great depths.

4) IMPORTANCE TO MAN. Food for sea animals and man, used in shoe polish, cosmetics, glue, confections, jellies. Agar is a gelatinous derivative of certain red algae; used as culture medium, as laxative, in clarification in liquors.

5) COMMON REPRESENTATIVES. *Nemalion, Polysiphonia, Chondrus* (Irish "moss").

6) EVOLUTIONARY IMPORTANCE OF RED ALGAE. The chief evolutionary importance of red algae lies in their highly specialized reproductive methods and in the definite alternation of generations which occurs in many of them.

SUMMARY OF ALGAE

1. Algae are the oldest and simplest green plants.

2. Algae lack roots, stems, leaves.

3. Most algae are adapted to life in water.

4. Blue-green algae are simplest structurally, brown algae are most complex.

5. The algae are a heterogeneous group of plants, the exact relationships of which are not known.

6. Include unicellular, colonial, and multicellular plants.

7. In lower algae, reproduction is entirely asexual. In others, isogamy occurs, and in more advanced types, heterogamy.

8. Isogametes probably evolved from zoospores which they resemble. Heterogametes probably evolved from isogametes.

9. Alternation of generations occurs in some algae, but is not generally well-established.

10. The green algae may be ancestors of higher plants. The brown and red algae are specialized terminal groups. The flagellates are possible descendants of the first living organisms.

11. The sex organs of algae are structurally simple.

CHAPTER XVIII

THALLOPHYTA: FUNGI

FUNGI AS A WHOLE

Fungi show many parallelisms with algae with respect to structure and function. Fungi lack chlorophyll; most species are saprophytes or parasites (or both); a few species make food by *chemosynthesis*, in which the oxidation of certain chemicals furnishes the energy for food synthesis.

Like algae, fungi lack vascular tissues and true roots, stems, and leaves, and they do not form embryos. The plants formerly classified together as "fungi" are now separated into three phyla: *Schizomycophyta* (bacteria), *Myxomycophyta* (slime molds), and *Eumycophyta* (true fungi).

THE FUNGI

I. **Phylum Schizomycophyta (bacteria)**

1) STRUCTURE. Unicellular, often forming sheet-like or filamentous colonies. Smallest organisms; average size is about 2 x ½ micron; some even smaller. Three shapes: spheres [1] (*cocci*), rods [2] (*bacilli*), and spirals [3] (*spirilla*). Rods and spirals often have flagella. Cytoplasm simple structurally; primitive nuclei present, simpler than those of higher plants. Have thin walls, often with surrounding gelatinous sheath (Fig. 39).

2) REPRODUCTION. By *fission,* which may occur as often as once every 20 minutes. If cholera bacterium maintained its most rapid rate of fission for 24 hours, about 4,700,000,000,000,000,000,000 bacteria would result from the original parent cell. This maximum rate is never main-

124

tained because of lack of sufficient food and accumulation
of toxic wastes. Sexual reproduction appears to occur
in some.

3) SPORE-FORMATION. Certain kinds of bacteria form resting spores, usually one spore per cell. Spores are very
resistant to unfavorable external factors which might kill
ordinary active cells. Some biologists do not regard this
as reproduction because usually a bacterium produces only

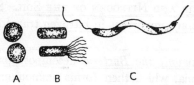

Fig. 39. Bacteria. A. Spheres. B. Rods.
C. Spiral.

one spore; thus, it usually does not increase numbers of
bacteria but is a method of carrying bacteria through an
unfavorable period. When conditions become favorable,
spores germinate, each growing into an active bacterium.

4.) HABITATS AND DISTRIBUTION. Most widely distributed
of all organisms: in air, soil, water, on and in other living
organisms. Chief requirements for their growth are water,
favorable temperatures, organic matter, and presence or
absence of oxygen (*aerobic* and *anaerobic* species).

5) IMPORTANCE TO MAN. Some activities of bacteria are
harmful to man, others beneficial. Beneficial effects much
more important.

a. *Harmful Effects*. (1) Cause diseases of man—
typhoid, cholera, pneumonia, lockjaw, tuberculosis,
etc. (2) Cause diseases of domesticated animals—
hog cholera, anthrax, tuberculosis, etc. (3) Cause
diseases of plants—fire-blight of pears and apples,
citrus canker, wilt diseases of tomatoes, potatoes,
melons, cucumbers, etc. (4) Cause spoilage of food.

b. *Beneficial Effects*. (1) Industrial uses—manufacture
of vinegar, cheese, alcohols, sauerkraut, silage, etc.
Curing of vanilla, tobacco; tanning of leather, retting

of flax, etc. (2) Decomposition of dead bodies and waste products of plants and animals. Organic compounds in these are broken down by bacteria and other fungi into simpler substances—CO_2, salts, etc. —which can be used again by green plants in food synthesis. Clear earth of dead bodies. (3) Maintenance of soil fertility, especially with reference to nitrogen (see 6).

6) BACTERIA AND NITROGEN OF THE SOIL. Several types of bacteria are important in nitrogen transformations in the soil:

Reduc (a.) *Ammonifying Bacteria* decompose proteins into ammonia, which then forms ammonium compounds in the soil.

Oxida. (b) *Nitrifying Bacteria* convert ammonium compounds into other nitrogen salts. There are two kinds of nitrifying bacteria: nitrite bacteria (*Nitrosomonas*) which convert ammonium compounds into *nitrites* (NO_2 compounds) and nitrate bacteria (*Nitrobacter*) which convert nitrites into *nitrates* (NO_3 compounds). *Nitrosomonas* and *Nitrobacter* make their own food from water and CO_2, using energy obtained by oxidizing ammonium salts and nitrites (*chemosynthesis*). Nitrates of all nitrogen compounds are most important in the nutrition of green plants.

Reduc. (c.) *Nitrogen-Fixing Bacteria* take nitrogen gas (which most green plants cannot use) from the air and build it into proteins. There are two types of these bacteria: those which live free in the soil (*Azotobacter* and *Clostridium*), and those (*Pseudomonas*) which live in the root tissues of green plants, chiefly legumes. The latter type usually forms swellings, known as nodules. Plants with such N-fixing bacteria on their roots increase the N-content of soils in which they grow.

Reduc (d) *Denitrifying Bacteria* convert nitrogen salts in the soil into gaseous nitrogen which escapes into the air. This process, especially common in poorly drained soils, causes a loss of soil fertility.

II. **Phylum Myxomycophyta (slime molds).**

1. STRUCTURE. Body is a naked mass of slimy, multinucleate protoplasm (*plasmodium*) which flows over substratum in amoeboid fashion and can ingest solid food (animal characteristics).

2. REPRODUCTION. Plasmodial movement ceases, spore cases (*sporangia*) rise vertically from plasmodium. Sporangia form and shed spores, each of which grows into an amoeboid, one-nucleate protoplast (*swarm spore*). These develop into flagellated protoplasts, which divide rapidly. These flagellated protoplasts fuse in pairs to form zygotes. Zygotes fuse to form plasmodium. Are chiefly saprophytes.

3. HABITATS AND DISTRIBUTION. On decaying logs, leaves, etc., in moist, warm woods. Widely distributed.

4. IMPORTANCE TO MAN. Cause some decay of organic matter, few parasitic species cause diseases of higher plants (e.g., club-root of cabbage).

5. EVOLUTIONARY IMPORTANCE. Have mixture of plant and animal characteristics. Probably derived from, or closely related to, flagellates.

III. **Phylum Eumycophyta (true fungi).** The bodies of most members of this phylum consist of fungous filaments, or *hyphae*, which are long, slender, cottony structures. A mass of hyphae is called a *mycelium*. The bodies of most species are multicellular, and most species possess some type of sexual reproduction, in addition to asexual reproduction by spores, budding, or some other asexual process. The cells of true fungi contain nuclei, a feature which distinguishes them readily from bacteria. The true fungi are usually separated into the four classes listed below.

III. **Class Phycomycetes (i) (alga-like fungi).**

1. STRUCTURE. Resemble certain green algae in structure. Bodies composed usually of hyphae which lack cross-walls and thus have the form of continuous tubes. These hyphae are multinucleate. Hyphae are not organized into bodies of

definite form but usually grow as irregular cottony masses upon substratum.

2) REPRODUCTION. Reproduce asexually by zoospores and ordinary spores. Sexual reproduction in some species is isogamous, in others, heterogamous.

3) HABITATS AND DISTRIBUTION. Some species are parasites and grow in the tissues of their host plants (*Albugo,* or white rust, on horse-radish, and *Phytophthora,* or late blight, on potatoes). Many species are saprophytic and aquatic; some of these (water molds or *Saprolegnia* and other genera) live on sticks, dead leaves, etc., in water. Some species are parasites on fish. Other species grow on fruits in transit, on bread, and other foodstuffs, whose decay they cause.

4) IMPORTANCE TO MAN. Cause diseases of several important plants (downy mildew of grapes, white rust of mustards, potato blight, brown rot of lemons, etc.), cause spoilage of food, diseases of fish, decay of dead organic matter, produce industrially important chemicals.

5) EVOLUTIONARY IMPORTANCE. Thought to be closely related to certain green algae, from which they have possibly developed.

6) COMMON REPRESENTATIVES. A common species is *Rhizopus nigricans* (black bread mold), which forms a mass of hyphae on stale bread, fruits, and other foodstuffs (Fig. 40). Some of the hyphae (*stolons*) grow horizontally over the substratum; these send other hyphae (*rhizoids*) into the substratum; other hyphae (*sporangiophores*) grow upright. The latter develop enlarged sporangia at their tips. Each sporangium bears numerous asexual spores, which are released by the rupture of the sporangial wall and which grow into new hyphae. *Rhizopus* also reproduces sexually by an isogamous process similar to that of *Spirogyra,* as follows: two hyphae in contact with each other form lateral protuberances which press against each other. A wall is formed

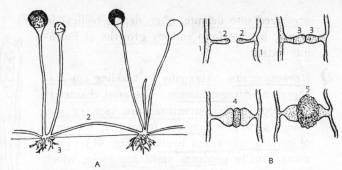

Fig. 40. *Rhizopus* (black bread mold). A. Portion of *Rhizopus* mycelium;
1. Sporangiophore with asexual sporangium and spores,. 2. Stolon, 3. Rhizoids.
B. Stages in sexual reproduction of *Rhizopus;* 1. Hyphae, 2. Progametes, 3. Isogametes, 4. Fertilization, 5. Zygote.

across each hypha a short distance behind the tip. The
protoplasm of each of these cells at a hypha-tip becomes a
gamete. The wall between these two cells breaks down
and the two gametes fuse. The zygote grows in size and
after a dormant period grows into a short sporangiophore,
with an asexual sporangium at its tip. The spores released
from the sporangium grow directly into new hyphae.
In *Rhizopus nigricans,* certain hyphae produce one kind
of gamete, others produce the second kind, a condition known as *heterothallism.* Only when both kinds
of physiologically-distinct hyphae are present does zygote-
formation occur. There are also *homothallic* algal fungi,
in which both types of gametes are produced on the same
hyphae.

Other common genera are:

Mucor—black mold.

Saprolegnia—water mold.

Plasmopara—downy mildew.

Phytophthora—potato blight fungus.

Class Ascomycetes (sac fungi). Largest class of fungi, with
about 40,000 species.

STRUCTURE. Most species have hyphae with cross-walls,
usually with one nucleus per cell. A few species are unicellular (yeasts). In some species, the hyphae have been

organized into definite, often fleshy, bodies; in others, hyphae form cottony growths of indefinite extent.

2) REPRODUCTION. Asexually by budding *conidiospores*, and fragmentation. The most characteristic reproductive structures are sacs, or *asci* (sing. *ascus*), which are formed at the ends of certain specialized hyphae (Fig. 41). Each ascus usually produces eight *ascopores*, which grow directly into new hyphae after their release from the ascus. Asci develop differently in different species. In Pyronema, antheridia and oogonia are present; an oogonium with many nuclei develops at the end of a hypha

Fig. 41. Ascus with ascospores.

and forms a trichogyne; a multinucleate antheridium forms on another hypha, comes in contact with trichogyne; intervening walls break down, protoplasm of antheridium moves into oogonium and fuses with protoplasm of latter; male and female nuclei pair off, each pair moving into a hypha, of which a number grow from oogonium; paired nuclei move into tip of hypha, are separated from rest of hypha by a wall; the two nuclei fuse, following which the fusion-nucleus divides three times, forming eight nuclei; the terminal cell becomes an ascus, the eight nuclei are surrounded by bits of cytoplasm and become ascospores. In some species, an oogonium may be present, but no antheridium; in others, there are no differentiated sex organs. Thus, in the sac fungi, there is a decline in sexual reproduction and sexual differentiation.

3) HABITATS AND DISTRIBUTION. Some are parasites, growing in the tissues of certain host plants. Some are saprophytes, growing in soil on decaying organic matter, spoiling fruits and other foodstuffs, etc. They are widely distributed on the earth.

4) IMPORTANCE TO MAN.

a. Cause many familiar diseases of economic plants— peach leaf curl, Dutch elm disease, chestnut blight, apple scab, etc.

    b. Industrial uses—manufacture of alcoholic beverages, cheese, "raising" of bread dough, etc.

    c. Food spoilage.

    d. Human food—truffles, morel.

    e. Decay of dead organisms and their wastes.

5) COMMON REPRESENTATIVES. The major groups of sac-fungi are:

    (a.) *Yeasts*—one-celled, non-filamentous. Reproduce chiefly by budding, less frequently by ascospores. Important in brewing, baking. Secrete an enzyme *zymase,* which converts glucose to alcohol and CO_2 (Fig. 42).

    (b) *Cup-Fungi*—hyphae organized into fleshy, cup-shaped ascocarps, inside of which asci are formed. Chiefly saprophytes in rich soil, decaying wood, etc.

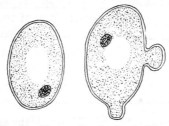

Fig. 42. Yeast cells, showing budding.

    (c.) *Powdery Mildews*—parasites, chiefly on leaves of green plants (lilac, clover, etc.) Form whitish patches of hyphae on leaves, with tiny black *perithecia,* which contain asci.

    (d.) *Blue and Green Molds*—chiefly saprophytes on old leather, jellies, spoiling fruit, potatoes, etc. Hyphae form indefinite growths, producing conidiospores and ascospores in large numbers. *Penicillium* is common blue mold, *Aspergillus* usually produces black spores. Some *Penicillia* are important in cheese manufacture. and production of penicillin, a bactericide.

    (e.) *Truffles*—have fleshy edible ascocarps.

(f.) *Morels*—cone-shaped, mushroom-like ascocarps.

6) EVOLUTIONARY IMPORTANCE OF SAC FUNGI. A close similarity exists between red algae and certain sac fungi with respect to reproductive structures and activities. Many botanists believe there is a close relationship between these groups. Others believe them to be descendants of Phycomycetes.

Class 3 Basidiomycetes (basidium fungi).

1) STRUCTURE. Have hyphae with cross-walls. In lower forms, hyphae form indefinite growths, in higher forms, hyphae organized into definite, often fleshy bodies.

2) REPRODUCTION. Most characteristic reproductive structure is the *basidium,* a club-shaped hypha, or terminal cell of a hypha, which produces usually four *basidiospores* on its surface on short, slender stalks (*sterigmata*). In some species, other kinds of spores are formed, but basidiospores are most characteristic of the group. There are no sex organs in basidium fungi, but there are nuclear fusions and reduction divisions involved in the formation of basidiospores; thus, basidiospores may be considered as originating from a sexual process. (Fig. 43).

3) HABITATS AND DISTRIBUTION. Many species are parasitic and grow within the tissues of their hosts. The saprophytic species are found in rich soil, on decaying logs, etc. The basidium fungi are widely distributed on the earth.

4) IMPORTANCE TO MAN.

Fig. 43.
Basidium with basidiospores.
A. Basidium.
B. Basidiospores.
C. Hypha.

   a. Edible species — some mushrooms and puffballs.

   b. Cause serious plant diseases — rusts, smuts, etc.

   c. Cause wood rotting.

   d. Cause decay of dead organisms and the wastes of other organisms.

5) COMMON REPRESENTATIVES. The chief groups of basidium fungi are:

(a) *Smut Fungi.* Parasites on cereal grains, chiefly infecting flowers and forming large numbers of black *chlamydospores* in the grains, which are often much enlarged and distorted. These spores usually rest till following spring, then produce short hyphae, each of which bears usually four basidiospores, which reach host plants and infect them, either in seedling stage or later in flowers. Basidiospores form mycelium in host. Smuts do much damage to oats, corn, wheat, and other cereals. Formaldehyde treatment of seeds kills smut spores.

(b) *Rust Fungi.* Parasites which cause serious diseases of wheat, oats, rye, and other cereals, pine, apples, etc. Called rusts because of reddish spores formed on surface of diseased tissues. Some rust fungi live on a single host, others require two different host species to complete their life cycle; the former species are called *autoecious,* the latter *heteroecious.* A common heteroecious rust is the wheat rust fungus (*Puccinia graminis*), the life cycle of which follows:

Hyphae in diseased wheat plants form, during the summer, blisters of orange, one-celled summer-spores (*uredospores*) which are carried by wind to other wheat plants, which they infect. Later in the season, the hyphae form, in dark-colored blisters, winter-spores (*teliospores*), which are two-celled, thick-walled, resting spores that remain on stubble and straw over winter. In the following spring, each cell of teliospore forms a short hypha which produces four basidiospores, which are carried by wind to leaves of the common barberry (not to be confused with the cultivated Japanese barberry). The basidiospores form hyphae in the barberry leaves; these hyphae in seven to ten days form flask-shaped *sper-*

mogonia, each of which contains hyphae with small cells (*spermatia*) at their tips. These are exuded onto the surface of the leaf by an opening in the spermagonium. These are two kinds of spermatia: *plus* spermatia formed from the hyphae produced by *plus* basidiospores, and *minus* spermatia formed by hyphae produced by *minus* basidiospores. When a spermatium of one kind meets a hypha of the other kind, fertilization occurs, resulting in the development of hyphae which produce cup-shaped *aecia,* which open on the lower side of the leaves. The aecia contain *aeciospores* which are carried by wind to young wheat plants, which they infect. Thus, the life cycle is completed.

Other heteroecious rusts are: cedar-apple rust (on cedars, apples, hawthornes, etc.), white pine blister rust (on white pine, gooseberry, and currant).

(c) *Gill Fungi*—mushrooms. Mycelium grows usually saprophytically underground or in decaying wood and periodically forms fleshy sporophores (*mushrooms*) of characteristic size, form, and color. A mushroom consists of ¹a stalk and an²umbrella-shaped cap, on underside of which are radiating *gills,* which bear basidia and numerous basidiospores. Mushrooms are classified on basis of spore color; there is no infallible rule for distinguishing edible from poisonous species (Fig. 44).

Fig. 44. Mushroom.*

(d) *Pore Fungi*—often similar to mushrooms, but underside of cap has pores within which basidia are formed. Common wood-rotting fungi, chiefly saprophytic. Some edible.

* Reprinted by permission from *Outline of General Biology,* by Gordon Alexander, published by Barnes and Noble, Inc.

(e.) *Tooth Fungi*—bear basidia on fine, tooth-like masses of hyphae.

(f.) *Puffballs*—spherical, pear-shaped, etc. Basidiospores borne internally, inside a tough surface covering. Covering ruptures or has a pore for escape of spores. Most puffballs are edible when young. Mostly saprophytic.

Class Deuteromycetes (fungi imperfecti). This group lacks sexual reproduction; at least, sexual reproduction of its members has never been observed. In their structure and asexual reproduction, imperfect fungi most often resemble Ascomycetes. The imperfect fungi include a number of species responsible for plant diseases and for human diseases such as athletes' foot, ringworm, and sprue.

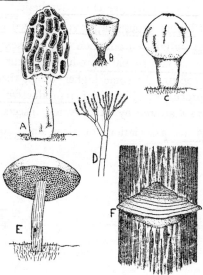

Fig. 45. Some representative higher fungi. A. Morel. B. Cup-fungus. C. Puff ball. D. Spore-bearing hyphae of *Penicillium*. E. Stalked pore fungus. F. Bracket type of pore fungus on tree trunk. (A, B, and D, are Ascomycetes; C, E, and F are Basidiomycetes.)

LICHENS

Lichens are associations of certain algae (blue-greens and greens) with fungi (chiefly sac fungi) in a state of *symbiosis* (mutual benefit). The fungi obtain food from algal cells, absorb and retain water, some of which algae use in photosynthesis. The algae and fungi usually reproduce simultaneously forming bodies composed of algal and fungus cells, which are capable of growing into new lichens. Lichens are common on rocks, tree bark, fence posts, etc. There are three main types of lichens:

1. FOLIOSE—flat, leafy or thallus lichens.

2. CRUSTOSE—are thin, hard crusts, especially common on rocks.

3. FRUCTICOSE—erect, branched growths.

SUMMARY OF FUNGI

1. Fungi are thallus plants; have no roots, stems, or leaves.

2. Fungi lack chlorophyll, and are chiefly parasites and saprophytes. A few species are chemosynthetic.

3. Cells of higher groups of fungi organized into hyphae.

4. In lower fungi, reproduction chiefly asexual. In higher groups, both asexual and sexual reproduction occur. Both isogamy and heterogamy occur. In some higher fungi, there is a decline in the sexual processes. The chief reproductive structures are spores, which are scattered by wind, water, insects, and birds.

5. Lichens are associations of algae and fungi living symbiotically.

CHAPTER XIX

EMBRYOPHYTA: PHYLUM BRYOPHYTA

The subkingdom _Embryophyta,_ which comprises plants that form embryos, are separated into two phyla: _Bryophyta_ (mosses and their relatives), which lack the vascular tissues xylem and phloem; and _Tracheophyta,_ which possess these tissues.

GENERAL FEATURES OF BRYOPHYTA

Bryophyta are the first green land plants. Small and inconspicuous, with some differentiation of tissues, but no definite xylem, phloem, cambium, etc. Some are thalloid, others have leaf-like and stem-like portions. They have _rhizoids_ which anchor plants and absorb materials from soil; rhizoids thus have the functions of roots, but differ from roots in that they are less complex structures. All Bryophyta have definite alternation of generations; the gametophyte is the larger, more conspicuous generation, the sporophyte is smaller, simpler, and partly or wholly parasitic on the gametophyte. The sex organs are _antheridia_ (produce sperms) and _archegonia_ (produce eggs), which are more elaborate than the relatively simple organs of Thallophyta. Fertilization occurs _inside_ the archegonium and the zygote develops in the archegonium; thus, egg, zygote, and embryo sporophyte receive protection and nourishment from archegonium and surrounding gametophyte tissue. Sperms reach the eggs in the pear-shaped archegonia by swimming through water. The Bryophyta are limited chiefly to shaded, moist habitats. There are about 23,000 species of Bryophyta.

Class Musci (mosses).

1) STRUCTURE. Mosses usually grow vertically, as compared with the commonly horizontal growth of liverworts. Mosses have a distinct stem-like structure, with small,

green leaf-like appendages; these are not considered true stems and leaves because they lack the characteristic vascular tissues of the stems and leaves of higher plants. The "leaves" of mosses have midribs which distinguish them from those of leafy liverworts. From the base of the stem-portion grow rhizoids which anchor the moss plant and absorb water and minerals. Moss plants rarely exceed six inches in height. The moss plant as seen with the naked eye is the major part of the gametophyte generation (Fig. 46).

2) REPRODUCTION. Archegonia and antheridia are borne at the tips of the leafy shoots, in some species at the same tip, in others on different plants. There are usually sterile hairs among and around the sex organs. The ovoid antheridia bear numerous sperms; each elongated, flask-shaped archegonium has a single egg. When mature antheridia are wet, the sperms emerge and move to the archegonia by swimming through water. Sperms swim down the canal of an archegonium, and one sperm fertilizes the egg, which

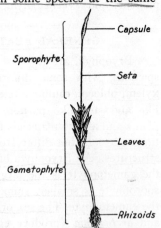

Fig. 46. Moss.*

then by growth develops into the young sporophyte within the archegonium. The *foot* of the sporophyte becomes embedded in the apex of the leafy shoot; the stalk (*seta*) of the sporophyte elongates; at the tip of the seta is the *capsule,* within which the spores are formed. On the capsule there is usually a lid (*operculum*). When the lid is removed, there is in most mosses, a *peristome,* or ring of teeth which bend outward when they are dry, scattering the spores, and bend inward when they are moist, pre-

* Reprinted by permission from *Outline of General Biology*, by Gordon Alexander, published by Barnes and Noble, Inc.

venting spore dispersal. The *calyptra* is the remnant of the old archegonium which covers the upper part of the capsule. Meiosis occurs in the capsule when the spores are formed; the spores are thus haploid and constitute the first stage of the gametophyte generation; when the spores are exposed to the proper environmental conditions, they germinate and form alga-like filaments of cells. Each filament is called a *protonema*. After a time, a protonema develops buds, from which the leafy shoots grow. These then produce archegonia and antheridia and the life cycle is repeated. The spores, protonemata, and leafy shoots with their sex organs and gametes constitute the gametophyte generation; the zygote, foot, seta, and capsule constitute the sporophyte. As in liverworts, the gametophyte generation is more conspicuous, larger, and more complex structurally; as in liverworts, the sporophyte depends on the gametophyte for its nourishment, either partly or wholly.

Asexual reproduction may occur in mosses by growth of new shoots from old shoots.

3) HABITATS AND DISTRIBUTION. Mosses require water for fertilization and are poorly equipped for conserving water; thus, they are limited to moist habitats. A few species grow in arid locations. Mosses are world-wide in distribution. Many of them grow on damp rocks, on the barks of trees, and in dense stands on the soil, producing familiar carpets of vegetation.

4) IMPORTANCE TO MAN. Mosses are of little direct importance to man. They are of some value in reducing soil erosion, they furnish food for certain kinds of animals. Peat-moss (*Sphagnum*) "leaves" have many large cells with circular openings; as a result, peat-moss absorbs liquids greedily and holds them tenaciously; this property makes it valuable as an absorbing medium used for preserving cut flowers, etc.; ground peat-moss is used as a lawn dressing; compressed, dried peat is used as fuel in many parts of the world. Mosses are of some value in filling in lakes and in aiding in the formation of soil.

5) EVOLUTIONARY IMPORTANCE. Mosses show many evolutionary tendencies similar to those of liverworts, from which they differ chiefly in their upright growth and their greater structural complexity. The mosses are usually considered as a terminal evolutionary group, which has given rise to no other groups.

Class Hepaticae (liverworts)

1. STRUCTURE. In most species, body is a flat, horizontal, branching, green thallus, with rhizoids growing from the lower surface into the soil. A liverwort thallus rarely exceeds three or four inches in length by one-half inch in width. Some species have partly erect bodies, with stem-like and leaf-like parts. Cellular differentiation is slight in most liverworts (Fig. 47).

2. REPRODUCTION. A liverwort plant, as seen with the naked eye, is the major part of the gametophyte generation. On this plant are produced antheridia and archegonia; these may be partly embedded in the thallus or borne on stalks rising from the upper surface of the thallus. In some species, the archegonia and antheridia are borne on separate thalli. At maturity in the presence of liquid water, the antheridia open and discharge their many motile sperms. These swim to an archegonium in which,

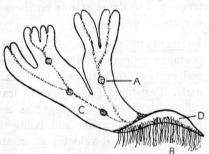

Fig. 47. Liverwort thallus. A. Sporophtye. B. Rhizoids. C. Upper surface. D. Lower surface with rhizoids.

at maturity, certain cells in the neck disintegrate, leaving a canal which extends to the egg-cavity (*venter*) of the archegonium. An archegonium contains a single egg. Several sperms may enter an archegonium, but only one fertilizes the egg. The fertilized egg (zygote) begins to grow and develops in the archegonium into the sporophyte generation, which is attached to the gametophyte by a *foot* and which consists, in addition, of a short stalk, with a *capsule* at its apex; the capsule is a structure of varying shape, within which spores are formed (Fig. 48). Meiosis occurs in the formation of spores, so that the four spores (*tetraspores*) produced from a spore mother cell are haploid. When the spores are mature, the capsule opens or disintegrates, freeing the spores, which fall to the ground and under favorable conditions, grow into new thalli. The spores are the first structures of the gametophyte generation, which is haploid; the gametophyte generation ends with gamete-formation (the gametes are haploid); the sporophyte, or diploid generation, begins with the zygote and continues until the spores are formed. The sporophyte is smaller, less complex than the gametophyte and is dependent upon the latter for food.

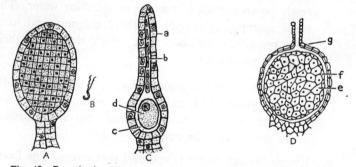

Fig. 48. Reproductive structures of liverworts. A. Antheridium. B. Sperm. C. Archegonium; a. neck, b. neck canal, c. venter, d. egg. D. Sporophyte; e. spores, f. sporophyte jacket, g. remnants of archegonium.

In most liverworts there is vegetative reproduction by *gemmae,* small, cup-like bits of tissue which develop on the upper surface of the thalli; when these gammae become detached from the parent thallus they grow directly into new thalli.

3. HABITATS AND DISTRIBUTION. Liverworts are poorly equipped for conserving water. Thus they are limited to moist places, usually away from direct sunlight. They live for the most part on soil, though a few species are aquatic. They grow in many places in the world.

4. IMPORTANCE TO MAN. Liverworts are of little importance to man. They may break the force of raindrops and thus reduce soil erosion. Some of them are colonizers of rocks, which other kinds of plants cannot inhabit. Some are used by animals as food.

5. COMMON REPRESENTATIVES. A common genus is *Marchantia,* in which the archegonia and antheridia are produced on separate plants on vertical stalks which arise from the upper surfaces of the thalli. An antheridial stalk bears a flattened, slightly concave disc at its apex; the antheridia are embedded in the disc and open at maturity onto the upper surface of the disc. An archegonial stalk bears a number of umbrella-like ribs at its apex; the archegonia are borne on the undersides of these ribs, with their necks pointing downward. Sperms reach the archegonia in running or splashing water. The small sporophytes develop in the archegonia and hang in a pendulous position, from which they drop their spores at maturity.

Another common genus is *Riccia,* in which antheridia and archegonia are borne on the same thallus; they are not borne on stalks as in *Marchantia,* but are embedded in the thallus near its midrib.

6. EVOLUTIONARY IMPORTANCE OF LIVERWORTS. The liverworts are the simplest true land plants of the present time. They resemble certain algae in their thalloid structure and are believed to have evolved from certain algae. However, they have made certain evolutionary advances over the algae: the development of multicellular sex-organs which protect the egg, zygote, and young sporophyte, etc. Though they are land plants, the liverworts are restricted to moist environments by their structural

simplicity, their lack of ability to conserve water, and their dependence upon water for fertilization.

Class Anthoceratae (hornworts). This is a small group of plants which superficially resemble liverworts. They differ from liverworts and mosses in being structurally much more complex.

SUMMARY OF BRYOPHYTA

(1) Bryophyta are the most primitive green land plants. Their simple construction and dependence on water for fertilization limit them to moist habitats.

(2) Sex organs of Bryophyta are multicellular.

(3) The sperms of Bryophyta are ciliated and swim to the archegonia through liquid water.

(4) Fertilization and zygote development occur within the archegonium; thus, the zygote and young sporophyte are protected and nourished by the gametophyte.

(5) Alternation of generations occurs in all Bryophyta. The gametophyte is larger and more complex than the sporophyte. The gametophyte makes its own food and also nourishes the sporophyte which cannot make sufficient food for its nutrition.

(6) The gametophyte generation begins with spores and includes liverworts, mosses, sex organs, gametes. The sporophyte generation begins with the zygote, ends with meiosis in the capsule during spore formation from spore mother cells. Spores are haploid and begin the gametophyte generation.

(7) Bryophyta probably evolved from some algal ancestor. Bryophyta are considered as rather specialized, though primitive, land plants which have not evolved into other types of plants. Their lack of vascular tissues prevents their reaching a large size and growing in any except a very moist habitat.

(8) The proportion of sterile (non-spore-producing) tissue of the sporophyte increases markedly from the most primitive liverworts through the mosses.

(9) In lower Bryophyta, there are no special mechanisms for spore dispersal; in higher types, there is the hygroscopic peristome which promotes spore dissemination.

CHAPTER XX

TRACHEOPHYTA: PSILOPSIDA

The phylum Tracheophyta includes all plants which contain the vascular tissues xylem and phloem. All these plants form embryos, and all have alternation of generations, in which the sporophyte is larger and structurally more complex than the gametophyte. The Tracheophyta comprise four subphyla, one of which is the *Psilopsida*. This subphylum consists chiefly of extinct plants known through fossils. Only three living species have been observed.

Structure. The plant body is rather simple, having a dichotomously branched stem but lacking roots. Leaves are usually absent or are very small. Rhizoids perform the functions of roots. No cambium is present, and thus there is no secondary growth.

Reproduction. The plant just described is a sporophyte, bearing sporangia on the stems. The sporangia produce one type of spore, which germinates on the soil to form a small greenish gametophyte. This bears archegonia and antheridia. Sperms reach the archegonia by swimming through water. Fertilization of the egg occurs inside the archegonia, and the zygote grows into an embryo sporophyte within the archegonium.

Habitats and Distribution. Extinct species grew in many parts of the world. The living species are tropical and subtropical land plants.

Importance to Man. Psilopsida have no economic value.

Common Representatives. Plants of the genus *Psilotum* are occasionally seen as curiosities in greenhouses.

Evolutionary Significance. Although this subphylum is so insignificant in the world's living flora, it is thought to be very im-

portant from the evolutionary standpoint. Certain features of
the structure and geological history of this group indicate that it
probably originated from green algae and that it is the source
group from which such groups of higher plants as ferns, horsetails,
club-mosses, and seed plants were derived. Among the important
fossil genera of this subphylum is *Rhynia;* from plants of this type
the higher groups of plants may have evolved. (See Fig. 53 in
Chapter XXIV.)

TRACHEOPHYTA: LYCOPSIDA

This subphylum includes about 900 living species, as well as many extinct species known only as fossils. The living species are usually called ⟨club-mosses.⟩

Structure. Living plants of this subphylum are rarely more than three feet in height; many are elongated creepers on the soil. They have vascular tissues, true roots, stems, and small leaves which are most often spirally arranged on the stems. Branch gaps are present, but there are no leaf gaps. Some extinct species were large trees.

Reproduction. A club-moss plant is a sporophyte, which bears sporangia on the upper surfaces of leaves clustered usually at the tips of stems in cones or strobili. The cones may be as long as two or three inches. Some club-mosses are homosporous (bearing one type of spore and one type of gametophyte), and others are heterosporous (having two types of spores and two types of gametophytes). Sporangia-bearing leaves are called sporophylls.

1. HOMOSPOROUS CLUB-MOSS—*Lycopodium.* Each sporophyll bears a sporangium with many spores, all alike. These spores fall to the ground and grow into small gametophytes on the soil. These are usually green, though in some species they are non-green and are saprophytes. The gametophytes bear archegonia and antheridia; sperms which are biciliate, as compared with the multiciliate sperms of horsetails and ferns, swim through water to the archegonia, within which fertilization occurs. The zygote develops into the young sporophyte, which has a temporary structure, the *suspensor,* which pushes the young sporophyte deeper into the tissue of the game-

tophyte, thus enabling the young sporophyte to derive nourishment more advantageously from the gametophyte. The suspensor is a structure formed in seed plants and club-mosses, but lacking from horsetails and ferns. The young sporophyte develops into the mature sporophyte which then produces spores.

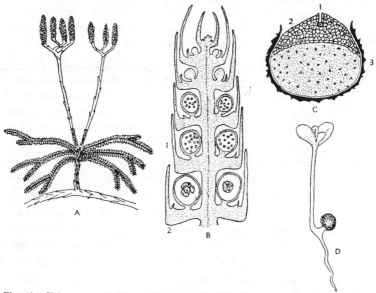

Fig. 49. Club-mosses. A. Plant of *Lycopodium*, with strobili. B. Longitudinal section of *Selaginella* strobilus; 1. microsporophyll with microsporangia and microspores, 2. megasporophyll with megasporangia and megaspores. C. Megagametophyte of *Selaginella*; 1. archegonium with egg, 2. megagametophyte, 3. megaspore wall. D. Megagametophyte with young sporophyte (*Selaginella*).

2. HETEROSPOROUS CLUB-MOSS—*Selaginella*. The sporophytes bear strobili of sporophylls at the branch tips. Each strobilus has two kinds of sporophylls, the lower of which are *megasporophylls,* the upper *microsporophylls*. These bear respectively *megasporangia* (one per sporophyll) and *microsporangia* (one per sporophyll). A megasporangium produces four *megaspores,* a microsporangium produces usually 64 smaller *microspores*. These spores are formed as a result of meiotic divisions of spore mother cells and are thus haploid. A microspore begins to grow into a *microgametophyte* (male gametophyte)

before it leaves its sporangium and the microgametophyte is formed entirely within the spore. The major part of the microgametophyte forms sperms; the microgametophyte lacks chlorophyll and depends for its growth upon food stored in it while it was still attached to the sporophyte. A megaspore begins to form a *megagametophyte* (female gametophyte) before the spore is shed from its megasporangium; usually the complete development of the megagametophyte takes place while the megaspore is still in the megasporangium, which remains on its megasporophyll in the strobilus. The microspores are shed and fall down to the megasporophylls, reaching positions on or near the megasporangia. When water reaches the microspores with their included mature microgametophytes, the microspore wall is ruptured and sperms are released. An opening appears in the megasporangium wall and the sperms reach the archegonia which are borne near the opening of the megasporangium wall. Sperms can reach the archegonia only by swimming through water. A sperm fertilizes an egg and the zygote begins to develop into the young sporophyte. The first division of the zygote forms two cells: the *suspensor* cell, which develops into the suspensor, and the *embryo* cell, which develops into the young (embryo) sporophyte deep in the tissue of the female gametophyte, from which the young sporophyte derives food. This development of a young sporophyte within the megaspore often occurs while the megaspore is still within the megasporangium. After a short time, the female gametophyte with its growing, attached sporophtye is shed and falls to the ground. The root of the young sporophyte enters the soil, leaves develop, and the sporophyte becomes independent of the megagametophyte. When the sporophyte reaches maturity, it then forms strobili, with two kinds of sporophylls, two kinds of sporangia, two kinds of spores, and two kinds of gametophytes. The most significant features of reproduction in *Selaginella* are: heterospory, the formation of strobili bearing two kinds of sporophylls, reduction in

the size of the mega- and microgametophytes, development of gametophytes *inside* the spores, retention of these
spores with their gametophytes inside the sporangia,
formation of a suspensor, dependence of the gametophytes
for nourishment on the sporophyte (Fig. 47).

Habitats and Distribution. Club-mosses grow in many
parts of the world, usually, though not always, in rather moist
places.

Importance to Man. Unimportant. Some ("ground pines")
are used in Christmas decorations. Lycopodium powder used in
fireworks and flashlight powders. Club-mosses of Carboniferous
helped form coal.

Common Representatives. See Reproduction.

Evolutionary Significance. Club-mosses show many similarities with seed plants—heterospory, suspensor, retention of
gametophytes within sporangia, etc. These indicate some relationship with true seed plants. Most botanists believe club-mosses are
a group parallel with seed plants but not so highly developed.
Lycopsida apparently evolved from Psilopsida, reached their zenith
in the Carboniferous Age, and are on the road to extinction.

Chapter XXII

TRACHEOPHYTA: SPHENOPSIDA

Like Psilopsida and Lycopsida, this subphylum reached its zenith in past geological ages and is doomed to extinction. Only 25 living species are known. Many extinct species have been discovered as fossils in rocks.

Structure. Sphenopsids have vascular tissues, true roots, stems, and leaves which are usually small and, in living species, scale-like. The leaves are whorled. Stems, which are jointed and hollow, are green and carry on photosynthesis. Living species contain silica, which gives them a harsh, rough texture. Most living species are not over four feet tall, but some of the extinct species were large trees.

Reproduction. A horsetail plant (*Equisetum*) is a sporophyte. Specialized spore-bearing leaves are borne in cone-shaped clusters (*strobili*) at the apices of the stems. Each sporophyll is hexagonal and bears five to ten sac-like sporangia, within which the spores are produced. Reduction division occurs in the formation of spores from spore mother cells. Each spore has attached to it two *elaters,* ribbon-like structures which open and wind with changes in atmospheric humidity and thus cause

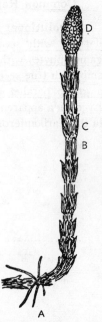

Fig. 50. Horsetail (fertile shoot). A. Roots. B. Stem. C. Scale leaves. D. Strobilus (cone).

spore-dissemination. The spores, which are all alike, fall to the ground and grow into *prothalli,* which are quite similar to those of ferns, except that they are usually more slender and often branched. The prothalli bear archegonia and antheridia similar to those of ferns. These sex organs may be borne on the same prothallus or on separate prothalli. As in ferns, the sperms reach the eggs in the archegonia by swimming through water. A sperm fuses with an egg to form a zygote, which, attached to the gametophyte, grows into the sporophyte plant; the young sporophyte is nourished for a short time by the gametophyte until it develops sufficient green tissue to make its own food. At maturity, the sporophyte forms strobili, the sporophylls of which develop spores; thus the life cycle is completed. In some species, the strobili are borne only on certain specialized branches.

Habitats and Distribution. The horsetails are found in many parts of the tropics and are also widely distributed in the temperate zones. They grow usually along river banks, around the margins of lakes, and frequently in ditches and along railroad embankments.

Importance to Man. There is little economic use of horsetails. Their deposits of silica make them useful as a scouring material; the dried, powdered stems are used in certain kinds of scouring powders. Some of the horsetails of the Carboniferous period aided in coal formation.

Common Representatives. There is only one genus (*Equisetum*) of living horsetails. In past geological ages, there was a much greater number of kinds of horsetails, which are now extinct. These ancient horsetails often reached much greater sizes than those attained by living horsetails.

Evolutionary Significance. Sphenopsida apparently originated from Psilopsida, reached their zenith in the Carboniferous Age, and are on their way to extinction.

CHAPTER XXIII

TRACHEOPHYTA: PTEROPSIDA

This is the dominant subphylum of the earth's present vegetation. The plants vary from small herbs to great trees. Most are land plants, but some species are aquatic. All have vascular tissues and true roots, stems, and leaves. The leaves, which are larger than those of Lycopsida and Sphenopsida, apparently arose by flattening and transformation of branch systems. (Leaves of Lycopsida are outgrowths from surface of stem; those of Sphenopsida are probably transformed minor branches.) The sporangia of Pteropsida are borne on lower surfaces or margins of the leaves.

Pteropsida are separated into three classes: *Filicineae* (ferns); *Gymnospermae* (conifers and allies); and *Angiospermae* (true flowering plants). The latter two classes, which produce seeds, are often called seed plants.

CLASS FILICINEAE (FERNS)

Structure. A mature fern plant is the sporophyte generation. It consists of roots, stems, and leaves, similar functionally and structurally to those of seed plants. The stems of most temperate zone species are horizontal and subterranean and are thus rhizomes. In some tropical species (the tree ferns) the stems are erect and trunk-like. The stems of ferns contain xylem and phloem, but usually no cambium; pericycle and endodermis surround each vascular bundle; sclerenchyma is located just beneath the epidermis and also in strands through the stems; parenchyma cells surround these other tissues, and epidermal cells form the surface layer and persist as the protective layer of the stem. The primary root lasts but a short time and dies when it is replaced by adventitious

152

roots from the stem. The leaves (*fronds*) of most ferns are compound; the leaflets are known as *pinnae,* the petiole from which they arise is termed the *rachis;* in doubly compound leaves, the leaflets of the second order are called *pinnules.* The leaves of ferns have an internal structure similar to that of seed plant leaves; the veins, stomata, and guard cells are much like those of seed plants. The leaves of ferns are green and make food; in most species, the leaves also produce *sporangia* (Fig. 51).

Reproduction. The sporophyte reproduces by spores formed in *sporangia* which are borne on the green leaves, usually on the underside, or on special leaves which produce sporangia but do not make food. The sporangia are borne in clusters called *sori*

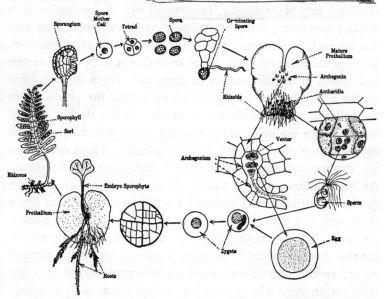

Fig. 51. Diagrams showing stages in the life cycle of a true fern (*Polypodium*).*

(singular, *sorus*) which appear as brownish dots or streaks on the leaves. A typical sporangium consists of a short stalk, with a compressed, circular, biconvex capsule at its tip; the capsule wall is one cell thick, with a row of thick-walled cells (the *annulus*) extending from the stalk about three-quarters of the way around the capsule. The inner and radial walls of the annulus cells are

* Reprinted by permission from *Textbook of General Botany,* by R. M. Holman and W. W. Robbins, 3rd ed., published by John Wiley & Sons, Inc.

thickened. At the terminus of the annulus is a group of thin-walled *lip cells*. Within the sporangium are produced *spore mother cells*, usually 16, which by meiosis produce haploid spores, usually 64 in number. As the sporangium matures, it begins to dry out; the annulus, because of its thickened inner and radial walls begins to straighten and tears the lip cells, rupturing the capsule and scattering spores. This movement of the annulus is often sudden and spring-like; with changes in atmospheric humidity, the annulus may undergo more bendings after its first movement, thus scattering more spores.

After being shed, spores fall to the ground and under favorable conditions germinate, a single spore growing by repeated cell divisions into a *prothallus* (gametophyte). A prothallus is a thalloid structure, usually heart-shaped and rarely more than one-quarter inch in diameter, resembling the thallus of a liverwort. It is one cell thick on the margins, several cells thick in the center, and usually grows horizontally on damp soil. From the lower side of the prothallus grow rhizoids which anchor the prothallus to the soil and absorb water and minerals. In the thicker part of the prothallus are borne antheridia and archegonia, both of which open onto the lower surface of the prothallus. These sex organs are smaller and simpler in structure than those of *Bryophyta*. An antheridium produces usually 32 sperms, which are set free by the rupturing of the antheridial wall; an archegonium has a short neck and a single egg in its base; when the egg is mature, the canal cells decompose, forming substances which attract the sperms. Sperms reach the archegonia only by swimming through water; several sperms may enter an archegonium, but only one fertilizes an egg. The union of a haploid sperm with a haploid egg forms a diploid zygote which develops by numerous cell divisions into the young sporophyte; the young sporophyte has a foot embedded in the gametophyte, by means of which it absorbs food from the gametophyte; the growing sporophyte soon produces a primary root, a primary leaf, and a small stem. The primary root and leaf disintegrate after a time, and the stem develops the adult leaves and adventitious roots of the mature sporophyte. The young sporophyte is nourished by the gametophyte until it develops enough leaf tissue to make its own food.

The sporophyte generation includes all parts of the life cycle beginning with the zygote, *to* the meiotic divisions of spore mother cells in the sporangia; the gametophyte generation begins with spores and ends at fertilization.

Habitats and Distribution. Ferns grow chiefly in shaded moist places, although there are some species which thrive in dry, exposed habitats. The greatest number of individuals and of fern species occurs in the moist regions of the tropics, where tree ferns often reach heights of 30 or 40 feet. Some ferns are limited to definite ranges of soil acidity or alkalinity.

Importance to Man. Living ferns are of little importance to man, except as ornamental plants. Some species produce abundant, long, epidermal hairs which are used as a stuffing and packing material. The trunks of tree ferns are often used for construction purposes in the tropics. Many ferns and their relatives of the Carboniferous period contributed largely to the formation of coal.

Common Representatives. Among the common genera of ferns are:

1. ADIANTUM—maiden-hair ferns.
2. POLYPODIUM—polypody fern.
3. POLYSTICHUM—Christmas fern.
4. CAMPTOSORUS—walking fern.
5. NEPHROLEPIS—Boston fern.
6. WATER FERNS, which are heterosporous, in contrast to the above homosporous genera. Common water-fern genera are *Marsilia* (water fern) and *Salvinia* (duckweed fern).
7. BOTRYCHIUM—rattlesnake fern.

Evolutionary Significance of Ferns. The ferns represent a line of evolution different from that of Bryophyta, in that their sporophyte is dominant and more complex and that they are better adjusted to a land habitat. The gametophytes and sex organs of ferns are simpler than those of Bryophyta. In some ferns there occurs *heterospory*, a condition found in all seed plants. The presence of heterospory, the development of complex xylem and phloem, and the retentions of the young sporophyte within the gametophyte indicate a close relationship between ferns and seed plants. It is believed by most botanists that seed plants probably evolved from some group of extinct fern-like ancestors. It is believed that ferns evolved from ancient members of the Psilopsida.

CLASS GYMNOSPERMAE (CONIFERS AND RELATIVES)

Structure. All species are woody plants, chiefly evergreen trees with needle- or scale-like leaves. Their tissues frequently contain resins and aromatic oils. Most species have a dominant main trunk, with much smaller branches.

Reproduction. Gymnosperms bear reproductive structures called *strobili*, or *cones*. A cone is a reproductive branch bearing usually non-green sporophylls. In most species, mega- and microsporophylls are borne on separate cones, called respectively seed cones and pollen cones; in most species, both types of cones are produced on the same plant. In a few species, both types of sporophylls are borne on the same cone. The details of reproduction in most Gymnosperms are exemplified by the genus *Pinus* (pines), as follows (Fig. 52):

1) CONES. In pines, the seed *ovulate* cones are rather large and woody, with woody megasporophylls (*female cone scales*). Each megasporophyll bears two ovules on its upper sur-

Fig. 52. Cones of the western yellow pine. A. Staminate cone, natural size. B. Ovulate cone, one-half natural size. C. Single scale from latter, bearing two winged seeds.*

face. The *staminate* pollen cones are much smaller than the seed cones and are not woody, with many small microsporo-

---

* Reprinted by permission from *Outline of General Biology*, by Gordon Alexander, published by Barnes and Noble, Inc.

phylls (*stamens*). Each stamen produces numerous pollen grains.

2.) SPORANGIA AND SPORES. An ovule is a megasporangium surrounded by an integument; inside an ovule is a megaspore mother cell, which, by reduction division, forms four cells, one of which becomes a megaspore. Each microsporophyll bears two microsporangia, inside which microspore mother cells produce microspores.

3.) GAMETOPHYTES. The megaspore inside an ovule undergoes many cell divisions to form the mega-, (female) gametophyte; this contains many food storage cells and several archegonia near one end of the ovule, the end in which there is present a tiny pore (*micropyle*). These archegonia are much smaller than those of lower groups of plants; each contains a single egg. A microspore grows into a few-celled micro- (male) gametophyte (dispersed pollen grain); pollination occurs at this stage, the developing male gametophytes (pollen) being carried from the dehiscing microsporangia of the microsporophylls to the ovules on the megasporophylls by wind. The gametophytes lack chlorophyll and are thus dependent upon the sporophyte for their nourishment. The formation of the two kinds of cones, the development of the microspores and young microgametophytes and of the megaspores and young megagametophytes, and pollination occur during the first growing year of cone formation. During the second year, the archegonia are formed in the megagametophytes in the ovules, fertilization occurs, and the seeds mature.

4.) FERTILIZATION. In pollination, the pollen grains are carried by wind directly to the surfaces of the ovules in the seed cone. When a pollen grain lands at the micropylar end of an ovule, it begins to form a tube during the first summer. Usually this tube is not completed during the first summer, but continues its growth during the next spring. Following pollination, the scales of the seed cone grow and are sealed together by pitch exuded from the cone; the developing ovules are thus held tightly inside the cone. The tube enters the micropyle, enters the nucellus (megasporangial wall) of the ovule, and discharges two sperms into an archegonium in the megagametophyte. One sperm fertilizes the egg, the other sperm and remaining cells of the pollen tube disintegrate. The fertilized egg (zygote) has the diploid chromosome number and develops into the embryo of the seed (matured ovule). The upper end of the embryo becomes a suspensor which pushes the embryo into the food-storage tissue of the female gametophyte, from which the embryo derives its early nourishment. Several zygotes may be formed in a single ovule, but as a rule only one embryo reaches maturity. Fertilization and seed development occur during the second year of cone growth; the scales of the seed cone separate at the end of the second year and shed their seeds, which germinate the third year in the soil.

5.) SEED STRUCTURE. A mature pine seed consists of the remainder of the nucellus, the seed coat, or matured integument, the endosperm, or food-storage tissue, which is a part of the female gametophyte, and the embryo, which consists of an epicotyl, a hypocotyl, and three to fifteen cotyledons. The germination of the seed is much as in flowering plants. (See Chapter XIV.)

Habitats and Distribution. Gymnosperms grow in many parts of the world. Some are found in the tropics, but their greatest development is in the cool parts of the temperate zones. They grow in a wide variety of habitats; some are desert plants, others grow only in regions of great humidity.

Importance to Man. Economic products of gymnosperms are: lumber (soft woods), resins, turpentine, tars, aromatic oils, tannins, ornamental trees, edible seeds, etc. Great forests of pines, firs, etc., are important in preventing soil erosion.

Evolutionary Significance. The living gymnosperms are the remnants of a formerly much larger and more varied group of plants. Many gymnosperms are known only in fossil form;

such species are now extinct. Some of these extinct forms had leaves and stems like those of ferns, but with sporophylls and seeds similar to those of modern gymnosperms. Such species were intermediate between ferns and seed plants and are sometimes called "seed ferns." It is believed that the modern gymnosperms evolved from such seed-fern ancestors. The modern gymnosperms are not considered as ancestors of the angiosperms but are regarded usually as a more or less parallel evolutionary group.

Common Representatives. Modern gymnosperms are separated into several orders, of which the more important are:

(1) CONIFERALES, or conifers, the largest order of gymnosperms, including pines, spruces, firs, cedars, Douglas fir, spruces, redwoods, California big tree, bald cypress, yew, etc.

(2) GINKGOALES, maiden-hair trees, belonging to the genus *Ginkgo*.

(3) CYCADALES, palm-like plants, generally considered the most primitive living seed plants. The sperms are ciliated, an unusual condition in seed plants. Cycads are dioecious.

CLASS ANGIOSPERMAE (TRUE FLOWERING PLANTS)

Structure. The characteristic structural features of angiosperms have been described in Chapters VI through XIV. As in Gymnosperms, the visible plants are the sporophytes; the gametophytes are tiny, non-green, and usually visible to the naked eye only with difficulty.

Reproduction. Reproduction in angiosperms has been described in Chapter XIII. There remains but to homologize the floral structures involved in reproduction in terms of alternation of generations. A flower, like a cone, is regarded as a specialized twig or branch, bearing reproductive leaves or sporophylls. The essential sporophylls are the stamens and carpels. Each stamen (microsporophyll) bears usually four pollen sacs (microsporangia), within which the spore mother cells and pollen grains (mature microspores) are produced. When a pollen grain carried by wind or insects reaches a stigma, it forms a pollen tube (microgametophyte), which grows down through stylar and ovary tissues until they reach the megagametophytes (within the ovules).

Each carpel (megasporophyll) encloses a number of ovules (megasporangia plus integuments), within which the spore mother cells
and spores are produced. In each ovule, one megaspore develops
into a megagametophyte (embryo sac). A microgametophyte sends
two sperms into the megagametophyte, within which double fertilization occurs, as described in Chapter XIII; the endosperm
nucleus develops into the food-storage tissue of the seed, the
zygote into the embryo (young sporophyte). As in Gymnosperms,
the gametophytes are non-chlorophyllous; they are very tiny, and
depend nutritionally upon the sporophyte. Reduction division
occurs in the formation of spores from spore mother cells and
thus the gametophytes are haploid; the diploid chromosome number is restored by fertilization, the sporophyte being diploid. A
striking difference between the megagametophytes of Gymnosperms
and Angiosperms is the lack of archegonia in the latter.

Habitats and Distribution. Angiosperms are the most
widely distributed of all green plants on the land areas of the
earth's surface. In addition, many species are aquatic.

Importance to Man. Angiosperms are the most important sources of foods, fibers, wood, rubber, drugs, and many other
plant products useful to man. They constitute the chief part of
the earth's vegetational cover and are most important as holding
the soil, nourishing wild and domesticated animals, etc.

Common Representatives. The Angiosperms are separated into:

(1.) MONOCOTYLEDONAE, which include cattails, grasses,
sedges, palms, lilies, irises, tulips, orchids, bananas, and
many others. The distinguishing characters of monocotyledons are: one cotyledon per seed, flower parts in
three's or multiples thereof, scattered vascular bundles
in stems, usually no cambium, and mostly with parallel-
veined leaves.

(2.) DICOTYLEDONAE, which include willows, oaks, elms,
maples, apples, roses, buttercups, petunias, phlox, violets,
sunflowers, etc. Distinguishing characteristics: two cotyledons per seed, flower parts chiefly in five's and four's,

rarely in two's or three's,[3] vascular tissues in cylinders or regularly arranged bundles,[4] cambium present,[5] leaves mostly net-veined.

Evolutionary Significance. The Angiosperms are the highest, most complex and apparently the most recently evolved major group of plants. They are best adapted of all groups of plants to a variety of environmental conditions. Some of them are very ancient, for Angiosperm fossils (e.g., willow, sassafras, etc.) have been found in old rock strata. Most Angiosperms are, however, apparently relatively recent plants. The woody angiosperms are generally considered to be older and possibly more primitive than herbaceous angiosperms. It is believed that Angiosperms originated from some now extinct group of gymnosperms.

SUMMARY OF MAJOR DIFFERENCES BETWEEN ANGIOSPERMS AND GYMNOSPERMS

(1.) Gymnosperms bear seeds exposed on the surfaces of sporophylls. Angiosperms bear seeds enclosed by inrolled sporophylls (carpels). A matured carpel-base (ovary) of an angiosperm is termed a fruit.

(2.) Gymnosperms bear eggs in reduced archegonia in their female gametophytes. Angiosperms have eggs free in their female gametophytes, with no archegonia.

(3.) In the pollination of Gymnosperms, pollen grains land directly upon the surfaces of ovules and thus the pollen tubes grow only a short distance. In Angiosperms, pollen grains land upon a stigma, and pollen tubes must grow a considerable distance through style and ovary tissues before they reach the ovules, which are enclosed by the ovary.

(4.) All Gymnosperms are wind-pollinated. Most Angiosperms are insect-pollinated, some are wind-pollinated.

(5.) The endosperm of Gymnosperm seeds is part of the female gametophyte and is thus haploid. The endosperm of Angiosperm seeds develops from the fusion of a sperm with two embryo-sac nuclei and is thus triploid.

(6.) Gymnosperms usually do not have sterile leaves associated with their sporophylls. Most Angiosperms have sterile leaves (sepals and petals) associated with their sporophylls (stamens and carpels).

(7) In most Gymnosperms, sporophylls are on separate cones. In Angiosperms, they are in the same cluster (flower).

(8) Most Angiosperms have vessels in their xylem, whereas such cells are lacking in most Gymnosperms.

(9) Gymnosperms are all woody perennials, whereas Angiosperms include both woody and herbaceous (annual and biennial) species. Annuals grow from seed and form seed in a single year. Biennials require two years from seed planting to seed production. Perennials live for several to many years, forming seeds each year after reaching maturity.

SUMMARY OF FEATURES OF SEED PLANTS

(1) The characteristic reproductive structures of seed plants are seeds. These are produced by cones or flowers. A cone or flower is a specialized reproductive twig.

(2) Seed plants are not dependent upon water for fertilization. A pollen tube carries the sperms to the eggs.

(3) The sporophyte generation is dominant and independent except for a brief time in its early development. The gametophyte generation is much reduced in size and structure, lacks chlorophyll, and is nourished by the sporophyte.

(4) Seed plants are heterosporous, producing microspores and megaspores, which develop respectively in microsporangia and megasporangia which are borne on microsporophylls and megasporophylls. These spores grow respectively into microgametophytes and megagametophytes.

(5) Megaspores are never released from their megasporangia, but develop into megagametophytes within the megasporangial walls. The zygote and young sporophyte (embryo of the seed) likewise are retained within the megasporangia. A mature seed is a megasporangium, with its integuments, which enclose the female gametophyte (or its remnants), the megasporangial wall (nucellus), the young sporophyte (embryo), and endosperm.

(6) Seed plants are the best adapted for life on the earth.

CHAPTER XXIV

EVOLUTION

DEFINITION

Evolution may be defined as a process of change. Organic evolution is the historic process of change by means of which organisms have reached their present state. Organic evolution may also be defined as the changes which result in the development of new types of organisms or the extinction of other types.

There are three chief types of evolution:

1. PROGRESSIVE EVOLUTION, in which there is an increasing complexity in structure and differentiation.

2. RETROGRESSIVE EVOLUTION, in which there is a degeneration or decrease in complexity.

3. PARALLEL EVOLUTION, in which different types of organisms show similar evolutionary changes, usually in similar sequence, often under similar environmental conditions.

EVIDENCES FOR ORGANIC EVOLUTION

Biologists agree generally upon the *facts* of evolution, but often disagree concerning the explanations of evolutionary facts. Evidences regarded by biologists as proofs of the phenomenon are:

Comparative Morphology (Anatomy). Studies of structure show similar developments in different types of organisms and thus indicate relationships. E.g., strobili of club-mosses and gymnosperms, archegonia of Bryophytes, Pteridophytes, etc.

Comparative Embryology shows similarities in origin and development in embryos of various plant and animal groups. E.g., similarities in development of young sporophytes of club-mosses, pine, angiosperms. In connection with embryology there should be emphasized the Biogenetic Law, which states that the development of an individual recapitulates the development of the race; e.g., the gametophyte of a fern is a thallus-like structure similar to the thallus of a liverwort or to certain green algae; the cycads have ciliated sperms similar to those of Pteridophytes, etc.

Geological Records, in the form of fossilized remains, show that different kinds of plants and animals have lived at different periods in the world's history and that there lived in past ages plants and animals which are now extinct. Many living plants show striking resemblances to some of these fossil species.

Comparative Physiology shows that certain physiological processes and products are very similar in certain types of organisms. E.g., photosynthesis in green plants, resins in conifers, glycogen in fungi, aromatic oils in mint family, etc.

Geographical Distribution. In closely situated islands, plants and animals are much alike; in more distantly separated islands, similarities are fewer. In regions shut off by barriers such as high mountains, wide expanses of water, etc., there are usually found certain species peculiar to that region but usually related to adjacent regions; it is believed that isolation leads to the development of certain types of organisms peculiar to the isolated areas.

Genetics and Selective Breeding show that new types of plants and animals can be developed. The appearance of mutations is evidence of changes in the nature of living organisms.

Artificially Induced changes by means of X-rays and other treatments are further evidence for the fact that living organisms are capable of evolution.

THEORIES ATTEMPTING TO EXPLAIN EVOLUTION

Lamarck's Theory of Use and Disuse (1809). When an organism uses an organ, that organ is increased in size and functional ability. Failure to use a structure results in its retrogression or disappearance. According to Lamarck, changes in environment cause certain organs to be used, others not to be used, and thus cause the building-up or atrophy of organs. These changes in organs, according to Lamarck, are inherited. There is no evidence for the inheritance of such "acquired characters," so this theory is considered as unimportant at present.

DeVries' Mutation Theory (1901). Mutations, or sudden unpredictable, heritable changes which occur in certain organisms, are thought by DeVries to be the chief method by means of which new types of organisms develop. Mutations are known to occur in many types of organisms, but the degree of their importance as causes of evolution is uncertain.

Darwin's Theory of Natural Selection (1859). According to Darwin:

1. Organisms produce more offspring than can ordinarily survive.

2. These large numbers of offspring result in a competition for food, or a struggle for existence.

3. Individuals or species vary in their fitness to compete in this struggle. Those organisms which are best fitted for this struggle survive; those poorly fitted are eliminated in the struggle.

4. The offspring of parents best fitted to survive inherit the favorable characteristics of their parents.

Some of Darwin's statements are correct, but objections have been raised to portions of this theory so that at present the theory of natural selection is only partly accepted. Modern theories of evolution emphasize the importance of mutations and the probability of natural selection among these mutations. Hybridization has also been regarded as a possible explanation of certain phases of evolution.

THE COURSE OF EVOLUTION IN PLANTS

The major evolutionary changes which have occurred in the plant kingdom are:

(1) The development of a nucleus in cells.

(2) Evolution from unicellular organisms to colonies to multicellular organisms.

(3.) Evolution of reproduction from asexual to isogamy to heterogamy. Development of alternation of generations.

(4.) Evolution of one-celled to many-celled sex organs.

(5.) Change from water to land habitat.

(6.) Development of vascular and strengthening systems.

(7.) Progressive development of sporophyte generation, retrogressive development of gametophyte generation.

(8.) Development of seeds, and fruits which enclose seeds.

(9.) Development of highly efficient vessels in angiospermous wood.

The supposed evolutionary tree of the major groups of living plants is shown in Fig. 53. It will be noted that the course of evolution is not represented by a straight line, but that a much-branched diagram is required to represent the supposed paths of evolution. The salient features of this diagram are:

1. The flagellates are possibly ancestors of both the plant and animal kingdom.

2. The red, brown, and blue-green algae are considered as terminal groups (groups which have not led on to the evolution of higher forms of similar type).

3. The position of the fungi is uncertain. Some botanists consider them as possible descendants of the flagellates, others believe that they have evolved from different groups of higher algae.

4. The green algae have probably given rise to the Bryophyta and, by way of the extinct *Rhynia* stock, to the club-mosses, horsetails, and ferns.

5. The modern gymnosperms and angiosperms are thought to have evolved from a group of fern-like ancestors, possibly those which produced seed-like structures in their reproduction. Modern gymnosperms and angiosperms may thus be regarded as somewhat parallel lines which have evolved from a common ancestor or from closely-related ancestors.

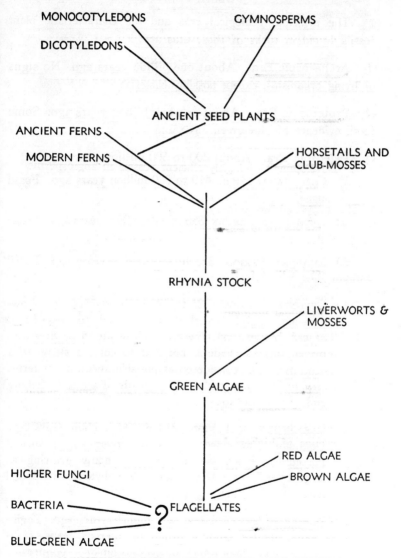

Fig. 53. A suggested scheme of the evolution of the plant kingdom.

FOSSIL PLANTS

The principal geological eras and the characteristic plant fossils found in rocks of those eras are:

1. **Archaeozoic Era.** About one billion years ago. No signs of living organisms, except possibly bacteria.

2. **Proterozoic Era.** About one-half billion years ago. Some fossil evidence of blue-green algae and bacteria.

3. **Paleozoic Era.** About 200 to 500 million years ago.

   1) CAMBRIAN PERIOD. 410 to 500 million years ago. Fossil algae.

   2) ORDOVICIAN PERIOD. 350 to 410 million years ago. Fossil algae.

   3) SILURIAN PERIOD. 325 to 350 million years ago. Fossil algae.

   4) DEVONIAN PERIOD. 285 to 325 million years ago. Low-growing, slightly-branched leafless and rootless *Psilophytes* (*Rhynia* and *Hornea*). Thought to be first land plants; bodies thalloid, but had vascular systems of a primitive type; considered as possible ancestors of ferns. In late Devonian rocks, many fossils of ferns, horsetails, and club-mosses are found.

   5) CARBONIFEROUS PERIOD. 210 to 285 million years ago. Dominant plants were ferns and their allies; ancient horsetails, club-mosses, seed ferns, many growing as large trees over 100 feet tall. Bryophyte fossils found here.

   6) PERMIAN PERIOD. 170 to 210 million years ago. Beginning of extinction of many carboniferous ferns, club-mosses, etc. Appearance of cycads, ginkgos, conifers.

4. **Mesozoic Era.** 60 to 170 million years ago.

   1) TRIASSIC PERIOD. Many ancient ferns and early gymnosperms became extinct. Ginkgo very common.

2) JURASSIC PERIOD. 120 to 145 million years ago. Beginning of development of modern types of ferns.

3.) CRETACEOUS PERIOD. 60 to 120 million years ago. (Decline of certain gymnosperms.) First appearance of angiosperms—willows, elms, magnolias, figs, beech, etc.

5. Cenozoic Era. Present time to 60 million years ago. The modern era in which the angiosperms have become the dominant plants. Extinction of many species by glaciation. Large increase in number of herbaceous species.

CHAPTER XXV

PLANT ECOLOGY AND GEOGRAPHY

DEFINITIONS

Plant ecology is the branch of botany which deals with the effects of environmental factors upon plant growth and distribution. *Plant geography* deals with the geographical distribution of various types of plants upon the earth's surface.

ECOLOGICAL FACTORS

Environmental factors which influence the growth and distribution of plants are:

Climatic Factors (Factors of the Atmosphere).

(1) TEMPERATURE. Temperature influences the rate at which the physiological activities of plants occur and thus influences plant growth and distribution.

(2) LIGHT. Light influences plant growth through its effects on photosynthesis, transpiration, direction of growth, heating effect, flower production, enzyme action, etc.

(3) CARBON DIOXIDE CONCENTRATION. Carbon dioxide concentration is the limiting factor in photosynthesis and thus changes in it affect the rate of photosynthesis. Excess CO_2 often inhibits growth.

(4) OTHER ATMOSPHERIC GASES. Gases from smelters, furnaces, etc., are often injurious to vegetation.

(5) WIND. Affects transpiration and also exerts mechanical effect upon direction of growth, form of plant, etc.

(6) ATMOSPHERIC HUMIDITY AND PRECIPITATION. Water vapor content of air, rain, snow, etc., are among most important of the factors influencing plant growth and distribution.

Edaphic Factors (Soil Factors).

1. AVAILABLE SOIL WATER. One of most important edaphic factors. Plants are often classified on the basis of their adaptation to water supply as follows:

   a. *Hydrophytes*—plants which inhabit water or very wet soil: cattails, water lilies, pond weeds, etc. Usually weak-stemmed, with numerous air spaces, often very fine, thin leaves, and little or no cutin.

   b. *Xerophytes*—plants which inhabit arid or semi-arid regions: cacti, sagebrush, Russian Thistle, etc. Leaves absent or much reduced in size, usually with heavy layers of cutin, well-developed water-storage tissues, stomata often reduced in number and sunken in pits, etc.

   c. *Mesophytes*—plants inhabiting regions with moderate water supply: common field and forest plants, such as roses, elms, maples, trillium, bluegrass, violets, oaks, etc.

   d. *Halophytes*—plants which inhabit soils with high salt content and which can absorb water only with difficulty, because of high solute concentration of soil solution. Halophytes often resemble xerophytes structurally because of difficulty of absorbing water: salt bush, greasewood, etc.

2. SOIL TEMPERATURE. Affects rate of root growth, respiration, water absorption, etc.

3. AIR IN THE SOIL. Roots normally require oxygen for respiration and thus a deficiency of air affects root growth. Waterlogged soils have little air and plants growing in such soils are usually badly stunted.

4. PHYSICO-CHEMICAL NATURE OF SOIL—acidity or alkalinity of soil influence rate of absorption, nature of materials absorbed, and other activities of roots. Presence or absence of essential mineral elements influences rate of food synthesis and other anabolic processes in plants, etc. Physico-electrical properties of soil particles affect absorption, drainage, etc.

Biotic Factors (Effects of Other Living Organisms)

(1.) GRAZING BY ANIMALS—removes food-making organs, causes stunting of growth, etc. Also, mechanical effect of trampling.

(2.) SOIL ORGANISMS—bacteria, other fungi, algae, protozoa, worms in soil are important agents in increasing or decreasing soil fertility, in altering physical properties of soils, in attacking roots of higher plants, etc.

(3.) INSECTS—which eat or otherwise injure plants or their parts or which function in pollination are important in growth, seed production, etc.

(4.) PARASITIC FUNGI—disease-producing fungi may stunt growth, form abnormal growths, and generally decrease populations of susceptible plants, often to the point of extinction in certain regions.

(5.) COMPETITION—struggle among various species of plants for water, soil salts, light, air, etc., influences distribution of plants.

(6.) SYMBIOTIC RELATIONSHIPS—certain plants may coöperate for mutual benefit, as, algae and fungi in lichens, nodule bacteria on legume roots, etc.

ASPECTS OF ECOLOGICAL BEHAVIOR

Plant Communities. A group of plants which live together under the same set of environmental conditions is termed a *plant community*. Many kinds of plants may be present in a community, but usually one to three kinds of plants occur in greatest abundance, as often indicated by such names as oak-hickory forest, beech-maple-hemlock forest, etc. There are many types of plant associations, such as pond communities, xerophytic communities, mesophytic communities, swamp communities, etc.

Plant Succession. Plant succession is a series of changes in the plants of a given region as a result of disturbances in climatic, biotic, or topographic factors. In a given region, the first community which becomes established is termed a *pioneer community*. As conditions change, such communities may be followed by *intermediate communities*, which are better adjusted to the newer environmental factors than are the pioneer communities. The intermediate communities are followed usually with further changes in external factors by a *climax community*, the highest type which can be supported by the obtaining set of external factors and the type which tends to perpetuate itself year after year under similar conditions (e.g., grasslands of Kansas, eastern U. S. deciduous forest, evergreen forest of Rocky Mts.).

A common type of succession is that from pond community to swamp community to wet meadow to wet thicket or forest to a mesophytic climax forest community. If a climax community is destroyed by fire or some other factor, the community will normally reappear by passing through the same series of changes.

Plant Invasion. This is the tendency for a species or an association of species to extend its regions of occupancy and thus to invade new areas. Invasion is a common phenomenon in plant successions.

PLANT GEOGRAPHY

Whereas ecology is concerned chiefly with present factors and their relation to plant distribution, plant geography is concerned, in addition, with factors of past ages which have been important in determining the geographical distribution of various kinds of plants on the earth's surface. The plant geographer relies upon such geological phenomena as the relation of the continental land masses to each other, the emergence and subsidence of land masses, glaciation, ocean currents, changes in the earth's temperature, etc., for the explanation of the facts of plant distribution. Important factors in geographical distribution, in addition to the climatic, edaphic, and biotic factors described in the preceding section, are *barriers* (oceans, high mountain ranges, deserts, etc.) which prevent or discourage the migration of certain plant species and *highways* (mountain passes, rivers, etc.) which facilitate the migration of species. Often a barrier for one species may be a highway for another; oceans are barriers to most species of plants, but are often highways to species with resistant, floating seeds or fruits.

Various plant geographers have divided the earth's surface into plant geographical areas on the basis of vegetational types, geologic history, climatic features, etc. It is impossible to describe

Fig. 54. Map of vegetation regions of North America.

in this outline all of these areas; only the plant geographical areas of North America will be treated, as follows (Fig. 54):

Tundra. Occupies the northern edges of North America, from Alaska to Labrador. Cold climate, with frozen soil, except for upper few inches in summer. Characteristic plants: lichens, mosses, grasses, sedges, other herbs, and a few shrubs.

Northern Evergreen Forest. Across continent from Pacific to Atlantic, south from tundra to Vermont, Great Lakes, and thence northwest through Canada and Alaska. Characteristic plants: chiefly conifers, such as black spruce, white spruce, hemlock, white pine, jack pine, balsam fir, etc.; some deciduous trees, such as aspens and birches, chiefly in cut or burned areas.

Deciduous Forest. From northern evergreen forest south along Appalachians to Texas and Louisiana, and westward from New York to Oklahoma, Wisconsin, and Minnesota. Characteristic plants: white oak, black oak, hickories, maples, chestnut, elms, walnut, ash, birch, tulip tree, and some conifers, such as short-leaf pine, hemlock, juniper, etc.

Southern Evergreen Forest. Coastal plain region, from Virginia to Texas, except Southern Florida. Characteristic plants: live oak, bald cypress, long-leaf pine, magnolia, gums, some short-leaf pine, etc.

Tropical Forests. Southern Florida, Central America, West Indies, Mexican coasts, etc. Characteristic plants: palms, *lianas* (woody climbers), orchids, mangroves, etc.

Grasslands. Texas to Manitoba, northwest into Canada, and west to the Rocky Mts., across Kansas, Nebraska, the Dakotas, etc. Characteristic plants: many species of grasses, asters, golden rods, sunflowers, etc. Relatively few trees.

Desert Regions. South from western Idaho and eastern Oregon through most of the region (The Great Basin) between the mountains of Colorado and Wyoming to the Sierra Nevadas of California and south Arizona, New Mexico, Texas, and Northern Mexico and Lower California. Characteristic plants: sagebrush, cacti, creosote bush, bunch grasses, rabbit brush, etc.

Rocky Mt. Forest. Southward from southeast Alaska and northwest Canada through Idaho, Montana, and the regions lying between the Grasslands and the Great Basin, extending south through the mountains of New Mexico into Mexico. Characteristic plants: western yellow pine, lodgepole pine, firs, western larch, some Douglas fir.

Pacific Coast Forest. The slopes of the coastal mountains, from southern Alaska into southern California. Characteristic plants: Sitka spruce, western hemlock, Douglas fir, western white pine, redwoods, western white cedar, arbor vitae, western yellow pine.

CHAPTER XXVI

THE IMPORTANCE OF PLANTS
IN HUMAN LIFE

The principal groups of products which are derived from plants and which are necessary, useful, or beneficial in human life are:

Fibers. These include cotton, common hemp, sisal hemp, Manila hemp, jute, kapok, flax, ramie, bowstring hemp, coconut fiber, palm fibers, and others. Some of these are derived from stems (linen, common hemp, jute, ramie); some from leaves (sisal hemp, Manila hemp, bowstring hemp, palm fibers); and some from fruits and seeds (cotton, kapok, coconut fiber). Principal products of fibers are: textiles, brushes, hats, baskets, chairseats, matting, upholstery and bedding stuffing, packing materials, string, twine, rope, nets, and caulking materials.

Wood Products. Fuel, lumber for construction and furniture making, fence posts, mine timbers, poles, pilings, pulpwood, cooperage, railroad ties, shingles, laths, veneers, plywoods, etc. Hardwoods are obtained from angiosperms, softwoods from gymnosperms.

Wood Derivatives, substances derived by chemical and physical alteration of wood. These include: charcoal, wood alcohol, acetate of lime, wood tar, wood gases, turpentine, oils, etc., all derived by wood distillation or wood extraction. Other derivatives of wood are: tannins (used in tanning hides), dyes, resins, essential (aromatic) oils, cellulose products (rayon, paper, pyroxylin, celluloid, artificial fabrics, cellulose varnishes), and drugs.

Tanning Materials, used in tanning animal hides to convert them into leather. Obtained from barks (hemlock, oak, mangrove, larch, Norway spruce, birch, willow, etc); from woods (chestnut, quebracho); from leaves (sumac); from roots (palmetto); from fruits (divi-divi).

Dyes and Pigments, obtained from woods (logwood, fustic, cutch, osage orange); from leaves (indigo, chlorophyll, henna); from roots and tubers (madder, turmeric, alkannin); from bark (black oak); from flowers (saffron); from seeds (annatto); from lichens (litmus). These are used for: dyeing textiles and leather, for paints, varnishes, paper, wood, and ink, and for adding color to beverages, medicines, and foods.

Gums mucilaginous, water-soluble substances developing chiefly from the decomposition of cellulose and other complex carbohydrates. Principal plant gums are: gum arabic, gum tragacanth, gum karaya, peach gum, and cherry gum. These are used chiefly in mucilages and glues, paper sizings, calico printing, painting glazes, as stiffeners in ice creams, meringues, and other confections, as an adhesive agent in pills, as a stabilizing agent for insoluble powders in liquid medicines, and as soothing agent in medicines.

Resins are water-insoluble, oxidation products of various essential oils, formed in wood and bark of many woody plants. Used in manufacture of varnishes, lacquers, paper sizings, sealing wax, incense, perfumes, paints, linoleum, ink, and in medicine as healing agents and antiseptics in salves and ointments.

Latex Products, derived from milky juice of stems and roots of various species of plants. Upon exposure to air or upon chemical treatment, latex solidifies into elastic or resilient substances, most important of which are rubber, chicle, gutta-percha, balata. Chicle is used in manufacture of chewing gum. Guttapercha and balatta are used for insulating submarine cables, and for the manufacture of machine-belting, golf balls, telephone receiver cases and mouthpieces, surgical splints, dental fillings of temporary nature, etc.

Fats and Oils. *Fatty oils and waxes* are true fats and oils and their derivatives, and are obtained chiefly from seeds, or less frequently, from fruits and leaves. *Drying oils* harden into elastic films on exposure to air. Include linseed oil (from flax seeds), tung oil, walnut oil, perilla oil, and others. *Semi-drying oils* form soft, solid films only after longer exposures to air. Include cottonseed oil, soybean oil, corn oil, sesame oil. *Non-drying oils* do not form solid films on exposure to air. Include olive oil, castor oil, peanut oil. *Vegetable fats* are solid or semi-solid at ordinary temperatures. Include coconut oil, palm oil, cocoa butter, nutmeg butter. Chief uses of oils and fats: foods, soaps, candles, linoleum, paints, varnishes, furniture and leather polishes, oil papers, waterproof fabrics, inks, artificial leather, illuminants, oilcloth, cooking oils, putty, laxatives, lubricants, cosmetics, massaging oils. *Waxes* are similar to fats chemically, but are harder; they are derived chiefly from leaves (carnauba wax) and fruits (wax myrtle) and are used in the manufacture of candles, wax varnishes, phonograph records, floor- and shoe-polishes, etc.

Smoking and Chewing Materials. Tobacco is the only important smoking material. Chewing products, in addition to chicle, include betel nuts, cola nuts, and coca leaves. Opium and marijuana are smoked illegally for their narcotic effects.

Drugs, used for many purposes in medicine. Include aconite, ginseng, ipecac, licorice, podophyllum, cascara, quinine, morphine, belladonna, ephedrine, digitalis, witch hazel, senna, croton oil, agar, ergot, and many others.

Beverages, used for pleasant flavors and often mildly stimulating effects. Include coffee, cocoa (cacao), tea, maté, and cola. The stimulating qualities of such beverages are chiefly attributable to alkaloids, such as caffeine.

Foods, used by man for his nourishment and for that of his domesticated animals.

1) GRAINS. The basic food plants of man. Include wheat, corn (maize), rice, barley, rye, oats, sorghum, kafir, milo, millets, etc.

2) LEGUMES. Peas, beans, soybeans, cowpeas, peanuts, lentils.

3) NUTS. Brazil nuts, coconuts, cashew nuts, pecans, walnuts, hickory nuts, hazelnuts, almonds, etc.

4) VEGETABLES from roots — beets, carrots, radishes, turnips, parsnips, sweet potatoes, yams, cassava; from underground stems — Irish potatoes, onions, taros; from shoots (leaves and stems) — asparagus, artichokes, cabbage, Brussels sprouts, broccoli, kohlrabi, celery, lettuce, rhubarb, spinach; from flowers or fruits (botanical fruits) — avocado, breadfruit, eggplant, cucumber, pumpkin, squash, tomato, okra, cauliflower.

5.) TEMPERATE ZONE FRUITS: apple, pear, apricot, cherry, quince, peach, plum, watermelon, muskmelon, grape, blackberry, raspberry, blueberry, cranberry, gooseberry, currant, strawberry.

6) TROPICAL AND SUBTROPICAL FRUITS: orange, lemon, grapefruit, tangerine, citron, lime, banana, plantain, custard apple, pineapple, mango, date, fig, guava, mangosteen, papaya, pomegranate, sapodilla.

7) SPICES AND OTHER AROMATIC SUBSTANCES used for flavoring foods, beverages, medicines, tobacco, and confections and for scenting cosmetics, soaps, and incense. Also used in medicine as carminatives and antiseptics. Among the most important plants in this class are: ginger, angelica, anise, cinnamon, sassafras, cloves, allspice, peppers, juniper, vanilla, dill, caraway, cardamon, mustard, nutmeg, mace, tonka beans, sage, peppermint, spearmint, thyme, bay, wintergreen, parsley, paprika, rose, citronella, lemon grass, lavender, jasmine, camphor, geranium, eucalyptus, orange, lemon, lime, rosemary, and sandalwood.

All the above economically-important plant products are derived principally from seed plants (Spermatophyta). Of the lower groups plants, living Pteridophyta and Bryophyta are of virtually no economic importance. The Pteridophyta of past ages, and some of their near-relatives, were largely responsible for the formation of coal deposits.

Of the lower divisions of the plant kingdom, the Thallophyta are of greatest importance to man. The algae, or chlorophyllous Thallophyta, are important chiefly in the following ways: food for human beings, food for fish and other animals of ponds, lakes, rivers, and oceans, food for protozoa, worms, and other soil animals, sources of fertilizer for soils, of medicinal iodine, of mucilaginous substances such as agar-agar and others used in culture media for bacteria and other fungi and for stiffening confections, ice creams, shaving creams, mucilages, etc. Algae are also important to man in a harmful or deleterious manner in that they pollute water supplies in which they produce offensive odors and flavors; in some cases, poisoning of cattle and other domestic animals has resulted from drinking algae-polluted water.

The fungi, or non-green Thallophytes, are exceedingly important economically. Among the beneficial or advantageous uses of fungi are these: food for man and other animals, production of vitamins, penicillin, ergotine, and other valuable drugs, manufacture of cheese and other dairy products, production of alcoholic beverages and of industrial chemicals such as alcohols, acetone, enzymes, organic acids, etc., sanitation of the earth's surface and maintenance of soil fertility by decomposing the dead bodies and waste products of plants and animals, the production of sauerkraut, vinegar, and other important foods, the retting of flax and other fibers, the removal of pulp from coffee and cocoa beans, the curing of vanilla pods, etc. Fungi are also important to man in a harmful or deleterious manner: they cause diseases of man (tuberculosis, pneumonia, leprosy, typhoid fever, lockjaw, various skin diseases such as athlete's foot, ring-worm, etc.), they cause destructive diseases of economically-valuable higher plants (wheat rust, corn-smut, apple scab, chestnut blight, wilt diseases of squash, tomatoes, cucumbers, potatoes, etc., potato blight, mildews of grape, peach brown rot, etc.), they cause the spoilage of foods (souring of milk, spoilage of meats, canned foods, fruits in transit), they cause the decay of wood, rotting of leather and fabrics and other objects rich in organic matter, and they cause many diseases of man's domesticated animals (cholera, pneumonia, anthrax, glanders, tuberculosis, etc.).

Plants also influence human life in less direct ways than those mentioned above:

    a. Plants provide food and shelter for wild animal life.

    b. Plants bind the soil and thus reduce or prevent erosion by wind and water.

c. Weeds reduce the yields of field and garden crops and disfigure lawns and ornamental gardens. Weeds compete with desirable plants for light, water, soil nutrients, and space, and thus reduce the growth and yield of the latter. Weeds may also mechanically injure garden and field plants by growing upon them and breaking off their stems, and they often harbor insect pests and pathogenic fungi which attack crop plants.

d. Poisonous plants are sometimes eaten by sheep, cattle, and other domesticated animals. They may cause violent illness, reduction in milk yield, abortion, poisoning of milk, and death of the animals.

e. Masses of vegetation influence the temperature and humidity of the atmosphere and thus may affect precipitation and other climatic phenomena.

The exploitation of economically-valuable plants has had many far-reaching social, political, and historical effects upon human life. For example:

1. The social and medical problem of drug addiction is based largely upon morphine, cocaine, and marijuana — all derived from plants. During the recent war, Japanese occupation forces in China encouraged the cultivation and traffic in poppies, since they knew that opium, derived from these poppies, would weaken the physical and mental resistance of the Chinese who made use of them.

2. The social problem of slavery was intimately associated in earlier times with the exploitation of cotton in the southern United States, of sugar cane in the West Indies, of rubber in Africa.

3. The potato famine in Ireland in 1845, which resulted from a serious outbreak of the potato blight disease, caused by a fungus, was responsible for widespread misery and death in that country and for the emigration of thousands of Irish people to the United States.

4. History's most famous mutiny, that against Captain Bligh, by the crew of the "Bounty," developed on a cruise which had as its principal object the introduction of an important food plant, breadfruit, from islands of the South Pacific to the English colonies of the West Indies.

5. The voyages of Columbus (1492) and of Vasco de Gama (1497) in an attempt to find a water route to India resulted in large part from a desire to exploit and control the trade in spices, sugar, and other valuable plant products of the Orient.

6. The expansion of Japan and Germany in Asia and Central Europe respectively was partly a result of overpopulation and the need for additional agricultural land to produce food. This was one of the major causes of World War II.

7. The crippling effect of the rubber shortage in 1942-1946 in the United States arose from Japan's capture of the world's principal rubber plantations, those in Malaya, Indo-China, and Sumatra, in early 1942.

8. Overproduction of crops has on many occasions (as, for example, in the United States in the early 1930's) resulted in unprofitable prices for farmers and gardeners and has led to such drastic economic regulations as destruction of crops, removal of acreage from cultivation, price subsidies, special taxes and tariffs, etc.

9. The miserable plight of migratory farm workers and share-croppers at various times has been related to agricultural maladjustments.

Review Examination

The following examination is designed to aid the student in reviewing essential facts and principles. It should also be helpful in preparing for a final examination. It is recommended that the student write his answer to each question and that he compare his written answers with the discussions in the Outline and also with one or more standard textbooks. The numbers in parentheses following each question refer to Outline pages which answer the question.

1. What is the subject matter of botany? (1, 2)
2. What did the Greeks contribute to the science of botany? (1)
3. List the 9 chief branches of modern botany and indicate the scope of each. (2, 3)
4. What are the main values to be derived from studying botany? (3)
5. State the 5 main features distinguishing living from non-living entities. (4)
6. State the differences between Mechanistic and Vitalistic philosophies. (4, 5)
7. List and criticize 4 theories concerning the origin of life. (5)
8. What 5 differences help to distinguish most plants from most animals? (5, 6)
9. State the main differences between the old and the new systems of plant classification. (7, 109–111)
10. State the functions of the 3 vegetative parts of seed plants. (9, 10)
11. How do flowers develop, and what is their function? (10, 82)
12. Explain the Cell Theory of Schleiden and Schwann and compare it with the Organismal Theory. (11, 12)
13. Describe the major parts of a typical plant cell. (12–15)
14. State the functions of the following: pectic substances; nucleus; cytoplasmic membrane; plastids; vacuoles. (13–15)
15. Describe the 5 simple permanent tissues and the 2 complex permanent tissues of higher plants. (17–19)
16. What are meristematic tissues, and how do they differ from the permanent tissues? (16, 17)
17. List the main features of a colloidal system. (20)
18. What are the most common chemical elements in plant protoplasm, and which of these are present in abundant quantities? (20)
19. What chemical compounds are found in protoplasm? (20)
20. Give 5 reasons why water is important in plants. (21)
21. Define: *imbibition; osmosis.* (21)
22. Describe the 4 factors which are basic to the process of osmosis. (21, 22)

23. Explain how living cells absorb water, and define the following terms: soil solution; osmotic concentration; osmotic pressure; turgor pressure. (23)

24. How does plasmolysis help to prevent the spoilage of foods? (24)

25. Explain the difference between passive and active absorption. (24)

26. List and define 6 important metabolic processes of plants. (25)

27. Describe the 4 phases of mitosis. (26, 27)

28. Define: chromosomes; spindle; cell plate; chromatin; amitosis. (26, 27)

29. State the 5 chief functions of roots. (28)

30. What are the components of most soils? (28–30)

31. What are the 3 general ways in which plants influence soils? (30, 31)

32. Define: embryo; hypocotyl; primary root; secondary roots; adventitious roots; root system; diffuse root systems; tap-root systems; nodes; internodes; pericycle; root cap; meristematic region; elongation region; maturation region; epidermis; cortex; endodermis; suberin; xylem; phloem; parenchyma; stele. (31–37)

33. List 6 main points concerning the physiology of roots. (37)

34. What are the functions of aerial roots, prop roots, storage roots, and contractile roots? (37)

35. What are 3 main functions of stems? (38)

36. Define: shoot; shoot system; aerial stems; subterranean stems; climbing stems; prostrate stems; herbaceous stems; woody stems; tree; shrub; buds; axillary buds; naked buds; whorled buds; adventitious bud. (38, 39)

37. Describe the growth of stem buds, indicating the structures which are formed. (39, 40)

38. Define: hairs; spines; lenticels; leaf scars; bundle scars; bud scars; twig scars; rhizomes; tubers; bulbs; corms. (40–43)

39. What are the main parts of a woody stem? (44)

40. List the primary and the secondary tissues of woody stems, stating the location, origin, structure, and functions of each. (44–49)

41. Define: annual ring; secondary rays; primary rays; cork cells; vessels; tracheids; springwood; summerwood; tyloses; sapwood; heartwood; dicotyledons; monocotyledons; closed bundles; leaf traces. (48–54)

42. Compare herbaceous stems of dicotyledons with herbaceous stems of monocotyledons. (52–54)

43. What is the evidence for upward conduction in the xylem? (55)

44. Describe briefly and evaluate 6 theories put forward to explain the ascent of sap. (56, 57)

45. What are the evidences for downward conduction of foods in the phloem? (58)

46. Describe pruning, girdling, and grafting. (59, 60)

47. What is a leaf, how does it develop, and what are the 3 common types of leaf arrangement on a stem? (61)

48. How do leaves vary as to: longevity, petioles, stipules, size, shape, venation, margins, and number of blades per leaf. (63, 64)

49. Describe the tissues shown in a microscopic cross section of a leaf. (65–67)
50. What is photosynthesis, and what are the 5 principal conditions necessary for its occurrence? (67, 68)
51. Define transpiration, state its advantages and disadvantages, and list the environmental and the internal factors influencing the process. (68, 69)
52. Define: guttation; hydathodes, xanthophyll; carotin; respiration; digestion; assimilation; bulb scales; tendrils. (69, 70)
53. Define: metabolism; food synthesis; digestion and respiration; food; water cultures; fertilizers. (72)
54. Describe the chemical characteristics and functions of 3 groups of foods. (73, 74)
55. Explain how different kinds of plants obtain and assimilate food. (74)
56. Describe the process of digestion, indicating also the 6 characteristic features of enzymes and the functions of 4 enzymes. (75)
57. Define respiration and list the chief differences between photosynthesis and aerobic respiration. (76)
58. Explain the process, chemical products, and economic importance of anaerobic respiration. (76, 77)
59. Describe the growth process and the internal and external factors influencing growth. (78–80)
60. Define: response; stimuli; positive response; negative response; excitation; taxies; tropisms; phototropism; geotropism; hydrotropism; chemotropism; positive tropism; nastic movements; turgor movements; presentation time; latent time; reaction time. (81–83)
61. State the nature and development of flowers and describe the 4 kinds of floral organs. (84, 85)
62. List the 9 ways in which flowers differ in structure. (86, 87)
63. Define: pollination; cross-pollination; meiosis; placenta; funiculus; locules; embryo sac; spore mother cell; micropyle; egg; synergids; polar nuclei; antipodals; sperm nuclei; zygote. (88–91)
64. Define: fruit; ovule; pericarp; mesocarp; simple fruit; aggregate fruit; multiple fruit; accessory fruit. (92, 93)
65. Draw and label a figure of a seed showing 3 embryonic structures. (94, 95)
66. Describe the process of seed germination and state the external and internal conditions influencing that process. Define dormancy and viability. (95–97)
67. List 8 methods of seed and fruit dispersal. (98)
68. Explain the difference between heredity and variation. (99)
69. Describe 3 common kinds of variations. (99, 100)
70. State Mendel's 4 laws. (101, 102)
71. Define: chromosomes; genes; diploid number; haploid number; hybrid; incomplete dominance; crossing-over; homozygous; heterozygous; phenotype; genotype. (102–106)
72. Describe fully 2 methods of plant breeding. (106)
73. Define: species; genus; family; order; class; division; phylum; bino-

mial system; Thallophyta; Embryophyta; Bryophyta; Tracheophyta. (108–110, 137, 144)

74. Name and identity 10 phyla of Thallophyta, 3 classes of Bryophyta, 4 subphyla of Tracheophyta, and 3 classes of Pteropsida. (110, 111)

75. Explain 2 main kinds of sexual reproduction and 5 methods of asexual reproduction. (111, 112)

76. Define: alternation of generations; gametophyte; sporophyte; reduction division; maturation. (113, 114)

77. State 5 characteristics of Thallophyta. (115)

78. Name 6 phyla of algae and describe them with reference to structure, reproduction, habitats, importance to man, and common representatives. (115–123)

79. Name and describe 3 phyla of fungi. (124–127)

80. Name, identify, and describe 4 classes of Eumycophyta. (127–135)

81. Define: lichens; foliose; crustose; fructicose; symbiosis. (135, 136)

82. What are the general features of Bryophyta? (137)

83. Name and describe 3 classes of Bryophyta. (137–143)

84. Describe Psilopsida as to structure, reproduction, distribution, importance to man, and common representatives. (144, 145)

85. Describe Lycopsida and define: homosporous, suspensor, microsporophylls, megaspores, microgametophyte, megagametophyte, embryo cell, heterospory. (146–149)

86. Identify and describe Sphenopsida. (150, 151)

87. What are the chief characteristics of Pteropsida? (152)

88. Name, identify, and describe 3 classes of Pteropsida. (152–162)

89. Define: fronds; pinnae; rachis; sporangia; sori; annulus; Adiantum; Camptosorus; Marsilia; strobilus; micropyle; stamen; Cycadales; Dicotyledonae. (152–161)

90. Describe the 3 chief types of evolution. (163)

91. List 7 kinds of evidence of evolution. (163, 164)

92. State briefly the theories of Lamarck, DeVries, and Darwin regarding evolution. (164, 165)

93. List 9 major evolutionary changes in plants. (165, 166)

94. Define: Archaeozoic; Proterozoic; Paleozoic; Cambrian; Ordovician; Silurian; Devonian; Carboniferous; Permian; Mesozoic; Jurassic; Cretaceous; Cenozoic. (168, 169)

95. Distinguish between plant ecology and plant geography. (170)

96. List 6 climatic factors, 4 edaphic factors, and 6 biotic factors affecting plant growth and distribution. (170–172)

97. Define: plant community; plant succession; pioneer community; intermediate community; climax community; plant invasion; barriers; highways. (172–174)

98. List and describe briefly 9 plant geographical areas of North America. (174–176)

99. List and describe briefly 13 groups of products derived from plants and beneficial to human life. (177–180)

100. State 5 indirect ways in which plants influence human life, and cite examples of the effects of economically-valuable plants. (181–183)

Index

Abscission cells, 70
Absorption, 9, 23, 24, 28
Accessory fruits, 92, 94
Acetic acid, 77
Achene, 93
Acquired characters, inheritance of, 165
Active water absorption, 23
Aerial stems, 38, 42
Adiantum, 155
Aecia, 134
Aeciospores, 134
Aerobic respiration, 76
Aerobic species, 125
After-ripening, 97
Agar, 123
Age, 78
Aggregate fruits, 94
Agronomy, 2
Air, 28; in the soil, 171
Albugo, 128
Alcohol, 77, 131
Algae, 7, 30, 109, 111, 115, 116, 166, 168; blue-green, 110, 116; brown, 110, 120, 123; green, 110, 117, 123; red, 110, 122, 123
Alternation of generations, 113, 114, 121, 137, 143, 153, 166
Aluminum, 20
Ammonifying bacteria, 126
Ammonium compounds, 126
Anaerobic respiration, 76, 77
Anaerobic species, 125
Anaphase, 27
Anatomy, 2, 163
Anchorage, 9, 28
Angiosperms, 9, 109, 152, 159–162, 166, 169
Animals, 5, 74, 166; geographical distribution, 164
Annual ring, 48–51
Annuals, 40, 162
Annulus, 153
Anther, 84
Antheridia, 118, 130, 137, 138, 141, 146, 154
Anthoceratae, 110, 143

Anthocyanins, 70
Antipodals, 90, 91
Apple, 9, 61, 64, 109, 160
Archaeozoic Era, 168
Archegonia, 137–142, 146, 154, 160
Asci, 130
Ascomycetes, 129, 135
Ascospores, 130
Asexual reproduction, 112, 139
Ash, 61
Aspergillus, 131
Assimilation, 4, 25, 70, 74
Athletes' foot, 135
Atracheata, 110
Autotrophic plants, 74
Autumnal coloration, 69
Auxins, 79, 81, 97
Axillary bud, 39
Azotobacter, 126

Bacilli, 124
Bacteria, 24, 36, 109, 124–126, 168
Bacteriology, 2
Banana, 62, 63, 73, 160
Bark, 25, 44, 49, 58
Barriers, 173
Basidiomycetes, 132
Basidiospores, 132, 133, 135
Basidium, 132; fungi, 132
Bean, 38, 52, 73, 95, 96, 97, 109
Bedstraw, 61
Beets, 32
Berry, 92
Beverages, 179
Biennial, 162
Binomial nomenclature, 111
Biogenetic Law, 164
Biogenic Theory, 5
Biotic factors, 172
Blade, 10, 62, 63, 65
Blight, potato, 129
Body cells, 102
Boston fern, 155
Botrychium, 155
Brewing, 131
Bryophyta, 9, 109, 110, 137–143, 154, 166, 168

188